Moreton Morrell Site

River Habitat Quality

the physical character of rivers and streams

in the UK and Isle of Man

by

P. J. Raven[1], N. T. H. Holmes[2],
F. H. Dawson[3], P. J. A. Fox[1], M. Everard[4],
I. R. Fozzard[5], & K. J. Rouen[1]

[1] Environment Agency
[2] Alconbury Environmental Consultants
[3] NERC, Institute of Freshwater Ecology
[4] The Natural Step
[5] Scottish Environment Protection Agency

River Habitat Survey
Report No. 2
May 1998

i

HIGH QUALITY

Main picture: an upland stream, Beinn Eighe NNR, Wester Ross

River Thurso, Caithness

Dhoon Glenn, Isle of Man

River Finn, County Fermanagh

River Teifi, Powys

Moors River, Hampshire

Highland Water, New Forest

MODIFICATIONS

Weed clearance

Straightened channel

Culverts

Concrete channel

Urban pressures

Flow regulation

Foreword

Rivers are an integral part of our landscape. They have profoundly influenced human settlement patterns and activities. In turn, their character, behaviour and quality have been modified by a whole range of activities affecting the channel and river catchment. Rivers are important not only for their great variety of historical and current uses such as drainage systems, providing hydroelectric energy and transport, but they are also of particular value for many people living in towns and the countryside who go angling, boating, walking, or watching wildlife. River habitats are important for biodiversity, not only supporting plant and animal species in their own right, but also acting as wildlife corridors, linking together other habitats such as woodlands which have been fragmented as a result of land-use change.

The long association between people and rivers, traditionally has had a local focus. Until now, the only truly national overview of rivers has been provided by reporting on chemical and biological measures of water quality. This Report presents, for the first time, the results of a major national survey describing the character and quality of river habitats and the modifications affecting them. It also identifies how this information can help sustain and enhance the biodiversity of our rivers.

In producing this Report, the Environment Agency, Scottish Environment Protection Agency, and the Environment and Heritage Service in Northern Ireland have shown an impressive level of collaboration. The result is that an important new dimension has been added to our understanding of the environmental quality of rivers - one of our most precious natural resources. We are sure that this Report will stimulate interest in specialists and non-specialists alike and, more importantly, help to underpin the work already being undertaken across the UK to protect and enhance the quality of our rivers.

Michael Meacher
Minister for the Environment, Department of the Environment, Transport and the Regions

Win Griffiths
Environment Minister: Wales

Lord Sewel
Minister for Agriculture, the Environment and Fisheries in Scotland

Lord Dubs
Minister for Agriculture and the Environment for Northern Ireland

Contents

List of Figures (continued)

Acknowledgements

This Report represents the culmination of an unprecedented effort by dozens of committed Agency staff, contractors and others who contributed to development of the River Habitat Survey (RHS) method and then carried out fieldwork to establish the baseline reference site network throughout the UK and the Isle of Man.

The development phase of RHS was underpinned by R&D projects 529, 530 and 611, funded by the National Rivers Authority (1994 - 96) and the Environment Agency (1996 - 97), and carried out by the Institute of Freshwater Ecology (IFE). Additional resources in 1995 and 1996 were provided by the Scottish Environment Protection Agency and the Department of the Environment for Northern Ireland.

Invaluable comments on draft versions of this Report were received from each of the external advisors on the RHS project board, namely Professor Ron Edwards (Environment Agency Board member), Professor Mike Clark (University of Southampton), Professor Malcolm Newson (University of Newcastle), Professor John Jeffers (Applied Statistics Research Unit, University of Kent) and Dr Phil Boon (Scottish Natural Heritage).

Other useful comments were received from Dr Andy Stott (Department of the Environment, Transport and the Regions), David Glaves (Farming and Rural Conservation Agency), Dr Catherine Duigan (Countryside Council for Wales), Professor David Harper (University of Leicester), Roger Thompson (Rivers Agency, Northern Ireland), Susanna Allen (Environment and Heritage Service, Northern Ireland), Bob Carswell (Department of Agriculture, Fisheries and Forestry, Isle of Man Government), Dr Paul José (RSPB) and Professor Stephen Ormerod (University of Cardiff). Environment Agency comments were made by Marc Naura, Adrian Taylor, Fran Bayley, Phil Griffiths, Andrew Heaton, Dr Alastair Ferguson, Richard Howell, Robin Crawshaw, Gary Murphy, Andy Wood and Dr Geoff Mance. The Report was word-processed by Emma Churchill.

Permission to use the following photographs is gratefully acknowledged: pearl mussel (Mike Hammett); allis shad (NHPA); water vole (RSPB, photographer - Mike Lane); River Roding (Photoair Ltd); River Skerne restoration (Northumbrian Water and Airfotos); giant hogweed, Japanese knotweed, Himalayan balsam (ICOLE, Loughborough University); diseased alder (Forest Research); Nepal sites (Geraldine Daly). All other photographs appearing in the text were taken by the authors and RHS surveyors.

Assistance, permissions and support from riparian landowners regarding surveys of both reference and benchmark sites is gratefully acknowledged, including the opportunities provided by the Isle of Man Government and Philip McGinnity (Salmon Research Agency, Westport, Co. Mayo) to visit sites in the Isle of Man and Republic of Ireland respectively.

Finally, particular thanks go to Michael Gravelle, Paul Henville and Peter Scarlett (IFE), for producing the tabulated data and the bulk of the Figures in this Report.

Summary

1   River Habitat Survey (RHS) is a method for assessing the physical character and quality of river habitats: it has been developed to help the conservation and restoration of wildlife habitats along rivers and their floodplains. Its main purpose is to provide river managers with information needed to sustain and enhance biodiversity, using catchment management plans and environmental impact assessment as two mechanisms for realising this objective.

2   The RHS system is based on information from a major baseline survey of rivers and streams in the UK and the Isle of Man. This has provided a geographically representative sample of habitat features and physical impacts associated with the 85,000km length of rivers classified for water quality. Habitat and other data were collected from 500m lengths of river channel, and more than 5,600 such sites were sampled during 1994 - 97.

3   This Report demonstrates how:

•   habitat quality is linked to the physical character of individual types of river;

•   the physical character of river habitats varies within a single catchment and between catchments;

•   habitat character and quality are affected by artificial modification of the channel and adjacent river corridor;

•   individual features of known wildlife interest, or combinations of them, provide the basis for evaluating overall river habitat quality;

•   physical characteristics can be used by interest groups other than wildlife conservationists to describe river quality in terms of their own particular requirements.

4   The main results from the baseline survey show that very few pristine lowland channels remain. The current extent of physical impact is highlighted by the following:

•   more than 80 per cent of lowland sites in the UK have at least part of the channel modified;

•   severe structural modification to the channel affects 3.7 per cent of lowland sites in England and Wales, 1.7 per cent in Scotland and 5.0 per cent in Northern Ireland;

•   altering channel structure to increase flow capacity, provide protection against erosion or regulate flow through impoundment can seriously impoverish the variety of both in-stream and bankside habitats;

•   there are few extensive wetland habitats remaining alongside lowland rivers, reflecting the efficiency of measures to drain floodplains for intensive agriculture and urban development;

•   habitat degradation is less severe in upland rivers and streams, but even so, almost 60 per cent of sites have physically modified channels.

5   Despite the extent of these impacts, river habitats, and in particular riverside trees, continue to make a significant contribution to the landscape as a whole. This is particularly the case where riverside trees occur along watercourses flowing through intensively-farmed and urban landscapes.

Chapter 1
Introduction

• purpose of Report • key definitions • the importance of river habitats • uses of rivers •
• wildlife importance • the need for assessing habitat quality •

About this report

1.1 This Report is for readers with a professional, educational or general interest in rivers and in particular their wildlife habitats. It starts by describing River Habitat Survey (RHS), a system for assessing the physical character and quality of river habitats and the impacts upon them. It then goes on to provide a unique snapshot of the state of stream and river habitats in the UK and the Isle of Man. In so doing, it highlights the occurrence of those features which provide good wildlife habitat and the impact of channel management and catchment land use which have modified and, in many cases, impoverished them.

1.2 Although the development phase of RHS has focused on the rigorous design and construction of a major information tool, the system has always been intended for practical river management purposes, and its applications are now the focus of the implementation stage. This Report will be important in alerting planners, engineers and conservationists to the opportunities for using RHS to help improve on current best practice for river management.

1.3 The results are derived from a baseline survey of individual 500m lengths of river, carried out during 1994 - 97. This involved a stratified random sample of sites throughout the UK and the Isle of Man, based on those rivers classified for water quality purposes. All the main Scottish islands, the Isle of Wight, and Anglesey were included in the survey.

1.4 This Report provides an insight into the main findings from a unique baseline data-set and the first of its kind worldwide. Since there are more than four million data entries on the RHS database, the results presented in this Report merely provide examples of what can be generated. Further detailed analysis is required to explore the data comprehensively and provide a more informed basis for habitat quality assessment.

1.5 The remainder of Chapter 1 highlights the importance of river habitats and the underlying needs for a method to assess their quality. Chapter 2 provides the technical background to RHS, outlining the principles, method, and approach, including how habitat quality and modification are assessed. Chapter 3 provides an overview of the survey results, whilst Chapter 4 focuses on four specific types of river, demonstrating how RHS can be used to compare habitat quality and impacts at a more regional level. Chapter 5 illustrates other applications of RHS, including its uses for both catchment-based descriptions of physical character and environmental impact assessment. It also covers quality assessment in a broader context. Conclusions about the effectiveness of RHS and the overall state of river habitats are presented in Chapter 6, which also identifies how, in association with other systems, RHS can contribute to integrated river basin management.

1.6 Key definitions used for the purposes of this Report appear in Box 1. In addition, there is an illustrated technical glossary, together with a list of acronyms. A free-standing summary fact-sheet is included for those readers who wish to have the main results to hand but do not need the technical background. Further copies of this fact-sheet are available on request. Separate, regional fact-sheets will also be produced.

1.7 For those readers needing further technical detail, key sources of information are referenced, by superscript, and listed in numerical sequence in the References section. An interactive CD-ROM version of the RHS database containing basic information relevant for schools and other interest groups is being developed and tested in 1998. In the meantime, the summary fact-sheet and this Report (as a PDF file) are featured on the Environment Agency's World Wide Web site.

Box 1 Key definitions used for the purposes of this Report.

Benchmark: a top quality RHS site specially surveyed for calibrating habitat quality of a particular river type.

Channel: a term used collectively in the text, and for HMS scores, meaning the course of a river or stream, including the bed and banks; RHS data can, however, be split into channel (in-stream) and bank features *(see Appendix 1)*.

Classification: the grouping of RHS sites with similar attributes, features, HQA or HMS scores.

Extensive: the occurrence of a feature or modification along at least one third of an RHS site; can be applied to the channel or individual banks.

Feature: a distinctive, readily recognised physical object or form recorded during an RHS survey *(see Appendix 1)*.

HMS (Habitat Modification Score): modification to the **channel** expressed as a score based upon the type and extent of artificial features at an RHS site *(see Appendix 3)*.

HQA (Habitat Quality Assessment) score: the habitat quality of an RHS site expressed numerically as a score based upon the extent and variety of natural features recorded *(see Appendix 2)*.

In-stream: that part of the channel covered by water in normal flow conditions.

Lowland: land below 200m, including all of England south and east of a line joining Start Point in South Devon and Flamborough Head in Yorkshire.

Reach: a length of an individual river which shows broadly similar physical characteristics.

Reference sites: those RHS sites specifically surveyed to establish a representative baseline sample of rivers and streams, known as the RHS reference site network *(see 2.12)*.

Riparian: bankside and immediately adjacent land.

River corridor: land to either side of the channel, extending to the limits of associated floodplain wetland or 50m distance, whichever is the greater.

River habitat: feature or combination of features associated with rivers which provides suitable conditions for sustaining riverine flora and fauna.

River type: descriptive term for rivers of similar physical character *(see Box 4 for determining river type)*.

Semi-natural channel: the absence of artificial modification to at least 90 per cent of the channel as recorded by RHS, **and** a resulting HMS score of 2 or less *(see Appendix 3)*.

Site: a 500m length of stream or river surveyed by the standard RHS method *(see Appendix 1)*.

Spot-check: one of ten locations at which physical and vegetation features of the river channel are recorded during RHS, using transect widths of 1m and 10m for physical and vegetation features respectively *(see Figure 2)*.

Sweep-up: the process of recording features at an RHS site to complement the spot-check data *(see Appendix 1)*.

Upland: land over 200m north and west of a line joining Start Point in South Devon and Flamborough Head in Yorkshire.

The importance of river habitats

1.8　River habitats are important for three main reasons: they form an integral part of the landscape; they play a significant role in many human activities; and they can support a rich variety of wildlife.

1.9　Their influence on the landscape and human activities is encapsulated in the following quotation from the Oxford Illustrated Encyclopaedia:

"Rivers are the most significant features of the Earth's land surface since, more than any other agent, they have influenced both the nature of the landscape and the location of human settlement."

1.10　The location of many villages, towns and cities is testament to this, since very few are far from running water, as a glance at any Ordnance Survey map of the British Isles will show. The proximity of many settlements to running fresh water means that many people have a strong affection for their local stream, burn, beck or brook. This often stems from childhood explorations to catch minnows or later-life leisure activities such as birdwatching, fishing, boating, walking the dog, or simply enjoying the timeless quality of flowing water.

1.11 The character of streams is imprinted on many peoples' minds from an early age, and landscape features are an integral part of the mental picture which determines an individual's assessment of 'quality'. The theme of quality is reflected in the higher prices for accommodation with pleasant riverside views, both in rural and urban areas.

1.12 The distinctiveness and intrinsic value of rivers is a subjective evaluation, often based on one or more key factors: the setting (town or open country); the amount (flow) of water; how clear (clean) it looks; and the variety of (natural-looking) features in and alongside the channel. What the casual observer is unlikely to appreciate fully, however, is the complexity of factors which have shaped the current river landscape, and that the character and quality of that landscape is a good indicator of what has been happening in the catchment as a whole.

1.13 Until significant human interference, starting with the early forest clearances about 4,000 years ago, the rivers of the British Isles had been shaped by natural forces, their character influenced primarily by the last Ice Age and associated climatic and sea-level changes[1]. Given the complex variety of geology, glaciation history, rainfall patterns, hydrology, catchment size, relief and natural vegetation, it would be surprising if the physical character of any two rivers was precisely the same, even without human interference.

1.14 Human activities, particularly in the recent past, have had a profound effect on the shape and behaviour of rivers. Water pollution, whether caused by sewage, industrial discharges, nutrient run-off, pesticides or accidental spillage, has always been recognised as an issue. However, stronger pollution prevention and control measures mean that overall, river water quality is better than for some time, although there is still considerable room for further improvement in some industrial areas[2, 3, 4].

1.15 A combination of physical alterations to the channel and land-use changes in the river corridor, although less well documented, has perhaps been even more influential and long-lasting. For example, rivers have been enlarged, straightened and deepened for land drainage, flood relief and navigation; re-routed or covered over to accommodate urban development and major transport links; diverted to provide power for mills; dammed for hydropower schemes and public water-supply reservoirs; used for the disposal and dispersal of waste effluent; modified by the transfer of water between river catchments; and their water abstracted to provide water for canals, industry and agriculture (Box 2).

A walk along the River Medway on a bright sunny day

© Photo Air Ltd.

The River Roding in Essex, re-routed alongside the M11

Ellington Brook, Cambridgeshire - a straightened channel

A river impounded for water supply - Clywedog dam, Powys

Some power stations use river water for cooling purposes

Box 2 Some activities which can directly and indirectly impact upon river habitats.	
Activities	
Land drainage	Urban and industrial development
Flood defence	
Channel realignment	Construction of transport links
River regulation	
Water abstraction	Intensive cultivation
Inter-basin water transfer	Livestock overgrazing
	Coniferous afforestation
Navigation	Forest clearance
	Open-cast mining and quarrying
Impacts	
Loss of channel habitat	Increased bank erosion
Wetland loss	Increased siltation
Overdeep channels	Increased nutrient input
Increased spate frequency	Artificial flow regime
	Reduced flows
Higher flood peaks	Dried up channels

1.16   Intensive agricultural land-use, made possible by land drainage, and often involving cultivation right up to the channel, has resulted in the loss of lowland floodplain wetlands and woodlands and this has greatly impoverished many river landscapes. In upland areas, pre-plantation ploughing associated with coniferous afforestation, and overgrazing by sheep can both result in increased siltation and bank erosion which degrade wildlife habitats[5].

1.17   River channels are dynamic, so they respond to artificial changes in flow regime, sediment supply and channel form by adjusting their size, gradient and shape. In many instances these changes may extend a long way downstream from the area of original impact. If channel shape or behaviour does not suit local land-use requirements at a particular point in the catchment, the traditional river management response has been to retain the artificial channel profile, thereby exacerbating historical habitat degradation and fragmentation.

1.18   Integrated river basin management at the catchment scale means working with nature rather than against it[6]. This is reflected in an increasing emphasis on efforts to restore those channel features, wetland functions and biodiversity lost through artificial canalisation.

1.19   Today, rivers are used for a huge variety of purposes. For example, in England and Wales:

*   36,000km of rivers are maintained for fluvial flood defence;
*   more than 50,000 million litres of river water and groundwater are abstracted daily by licence holders for public water supply, agricultural and industrial use; and
*   1,500km of rivers are used for navigation[7].

1.20   Recreational use of rivers is extremely popular. For instance, more than 200 million leisure visits are made to rivers each year[8]. More than three million anglers go fishing at least once a year in Great Britain, and in so doing, spend £2.9bn[9]. In Scotland, salmon fishing is estimated to be worth £70m annually to the rural economy. There are an estimated 100,000 regular canoeists in Britain and 29,000 licensed pleasure craft use the River Thames alone[7].

1.21   Given the historical and current pressures on the landscape as a whole, it is not surprising that rivers represent an important refuge for wildlife. The total length of UK rivers and streams mapped at 1:50,000 scale is approximately 250,000km and there are many unmapped streams. This represents an extensive network of wildlife corridors, a function of particular significance in urban and predominantly arable areas. By comparison, the length of hedgerow in the UK is estimated at 500,000km.

1.22   Otter *Lutra lutra*, water vole *Arvicola terrestris*, freshwater pearl mussel *Margaritifera margaritifera*, white-legged damselfly *Platycnemis pennipes*, allis shad *Alosa alosa*, twaite shad *Alosa fallax*, and flowering rush *Butomus umbellatus* are just a few examples of animals and plants which rely on suitable river habitat conditions, as well as good water quality, for their survival. Rivers also support habitats such as riparian woodlands which are important in their own right. In England and Wales,

Woodland loss - the same stream at points 100m apart

Northumbrian Water/Airfotos

Restoring lost channel features - reinstated meanders on the River Skerne, Darlington

Recreational uses of rivers

38 rivers are protected within Sites of Special Scientific Interest (SSSIs) on the basis of their wildlife interest, the combined notified length totalling almost 2,400km. Some of these SSSIs are of international importance, qualifying as European Special Areas of Conservation (SACs) on the basis of their aquatic flora or fauna.

1.23   There are also fluvial SSSIs designated specifically for their geomorphological interest, and these too have an important link to wildlife habitats. Rivers also represent major landscape features in many Areas of Outstanding Natural Beauty, National Scenic Areas, Natural Heritage Areas and National Parks.

Water vole

White-legged damselflies on bur-reed

Allis shad

Freshwater pearl mussels

Some examples of riverine wildlife

Flowering rush

The need for assessing habitat quality

1.24   Organisations such as the Environment Agency, which are involved in the protection and management of water, need to operate in a coherent way through integrated river basin management. One of the stumbling blocks to full realisation of this approach has been the lack of a system to characterise and classify the physical structure of rivers. Such a system is needed to complement those already developed for reporting on water quality, based on chemical and biological sampling[2]. Without this capability, it is difficult to set targets for habitat quality, or to measure the impact (both negative and positive) of river channel management.

1.25   Recent development of the General Quality Assessment (GQA) scheme allows for reporting on other aspects of the quality of rivers, including invertebrate biology, nutrients and aesthetic quality[10]. Since physical structure is one of the primary factors which determines the type of aquatic biological communities present in a river, an assessment and reporting mechanism for habitats has been long overdue. This is particularly so in the context of promoting sustainable river management.

1.26   Some form of monitoring changes in habitat quality is soon likely to be a statutory requirement. For instance, the draft European Framework Directive on Water Policy has a reporting requirement for the physical as well as chemical and biological conditions of inland waters, to determine whether they are achieving 'good ecological status'[11]. The Directive will require that national reporting systems adopted by individual European Union (EU) Member States must be notified to the scientific community and that the details are published.

1.27   Under the Species and Habitats Directive (92/43/EEC), EU Member States are required to identify and designate SACs and to prevent deterioration in their conservation status. In so doing, there is a monitoring requirement with a view to maintaining, or where necessary restoring, 'favourable conservation status'. The ecological quality of rivers within SACs needs to be reported as part of this process. In addition, Article 10 of the Directive identifies rivers as one of the linking features which will encourage the coherence of the *Natura 2000* network, comprising both SACs and Special Protection Areas (SPAs), the latter designated under the Birds Directive (79/409/EEC).

1.28   In the near future, local planning authorities will need to judge whether or not development proposals will have a significant effect on the environment. This is a requirement of the EU Environmental Impact Assessment Directive (85/337/EEC), as amended by EU Directive 97/11/EC. Inevitably, some decisions will involve proposals that alter the physical structure of river channels. The basis of 'significant effect' therefore needs to take full account of all available information and quality measures.

1.29   The UK Biodiversity Action Plan places significant emphasis on the need to monitor and report on biodiversity, and a number of the key species identified as requiring priority action depend on rivers[12]. Using physical structure as a surrogate indicator of biodiversity is likely to feature as part of the reporting on key habitats such as chalk rivers[13]. The physical structure of rivers could also be used as a measure of sustainability in the context of maintaining or restoring conservation interest and reversing the wider effects of habitat fragmentation.

1.30   Given all these requirements, the lack of a system to assess river habitat quality is somewhat surprising, particularly in the light of other methods to classify rivers on the basis of, for example, the type of aquatic invertebrate and fish communities present[14, 15].

1.31   This does not mean that river habitats have been ignored. Indeed, the mapping of habitats and plant communities for river corridor surveys has, since the mid-1980s, been the main tool for helping to sustain and further the conservation interest of rivers maintained for flood defence purposes in the UK[16]. Although these map-based surveys provide a descriptive basis for an assessment of river habitat quality in a local or regional context, results cannot easily be quantified or compared in a wider geographical context.

1.32   River habitats may also have been taken so much for granted, that a system for quality assessment has, until now, not been considered necessary. However, the ever-increasing pressures on rivers, together with a new emphasis on cost-benefit considerations, means that a method for habitat quality assessment is required so that policy and operational decisions can be taken on a more informed and consistent basis.

Chapter 2
River Habitat Survey

• approach and methods • baseline reference sites • habitat quality assessment • river types •
• benchmarks • habitat modification •

What is RHS?

2.1   RHS is a system for assessing the character and quality of rivers based on their physical structure[17]. It has four distinct components: (i) a standard method for field survey; (ii) a computer database, for entering results from survey sites and comparing them with information from other sites throughout the UK and the Isle of Man; (iii) a suite of methods for assessing habitat quality; and (iv) a method for describing the extent of artificial channel modification.

2.2   Habitat quality is determined according to the occurrence and diversity of habitat features of known value for wildlife, and is derived by comparing observed features at a site with those recorded at sites from rivers of similar character (Figure 1). Habitat features associated with high quality are generally to be found at sites in a predominantly unmodified physical state.

Figure 1 An introduction to how RHS works.

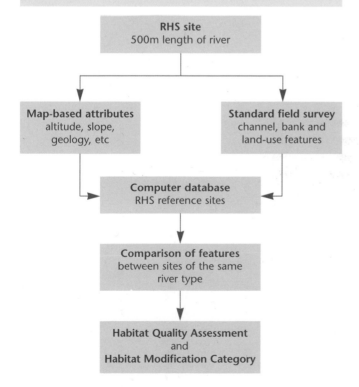

2.3   For the RHS system to be successful, it needed to:

• produce outputs easily understood and used by river and floodplain managers;
• be a tried-and-tested field method, compatible with existing methods such as river corridor surveys, for use in environmental and post-project appraisal;
• be based on a representative sample of river habitat features;
• have a computer database capable of deriving statistically valid systems for classification;
• facilitate the description and comparison of physical structure and habitat quality at catchment, regional, and national scales;
• be accepted by external organisations, notably the conservation agencies;
• with European Directives in mind, have applicability throughout the UK and beyond.

Field method

2.4   RHS is a systematic framework for the collection and analysis of data associated with the physical structure of watercourses. Data collection is based on a standard 500m length of river channel. The RHS form is four pages long and is simple to fill in (Appendix 1). Map information collected for each site includes grid reference, altitude, slope, geology, height of source and distance from source. During the field survey, features of the channel (both in-stream and banks), and adjacent river corridor are recorded (Box 3). Both the map-derived data and field data are computerised, allowing easy access to a database and rapid analysis of the information collected.

2.5   Building on the experience of river corridor surveys, the field method has been developed and refined by extensive field trials and subsequent analysis of data. RHS does not require specialist geomorphological or botanical expertise, but because

Features recorded	At 10 spot-checks	In sweep-up
Predominant valley form		✓
Predominant channel substrate	✓	
Predominant bank material	✓	
Flow type(s) and associated features	✓	✓
Channel and bank modifications	✓	✓
Bankface and banktop vegetation structure	✓	
Channel vegetation types	✓	✓
Bank profile (unmodified and modified)		✓
Bankside trees and associated features		✓
Channel habitat features	✓	✓
Artificial features	✓	✓
Features of special interest		✓
Land use	✓	✓

it relies on observational data, consistent recognition of features included on the field survey form is essential. To achieve this, an illustrated survey manual and accompanying video have been produced, and RHS field surveyors have to be trained, tested and accredited at approved courses[18].

2.6　To test further for consistency, 38 RHS sites were visited by experienced and novice surveyors. Comparing the results from individual data entries established the variation in the recording of features by individual surveyors and this information was used to improve training methods and specify the RHS accreditation test[19].

2.7　Channel substrate, habitat features, aquatic vegetation types, the complexity of bank vegetation structure and the type of artificial modification to the channel and banks are recorded at each of 10 *spot-checks* located at 50m intervals (Figure 2). The recording format is simple, and a two-letter abbreviation for each feature is used. These abbreviations are included on both the form and a laminated spot-check key, acting as a prompt for the surveyor (Appendix 1).

2.8　A *sweep-up* checklist is also completed to ensure that features and modifications not occurring

Figure 2 Features recorded at RHS spot-checks.

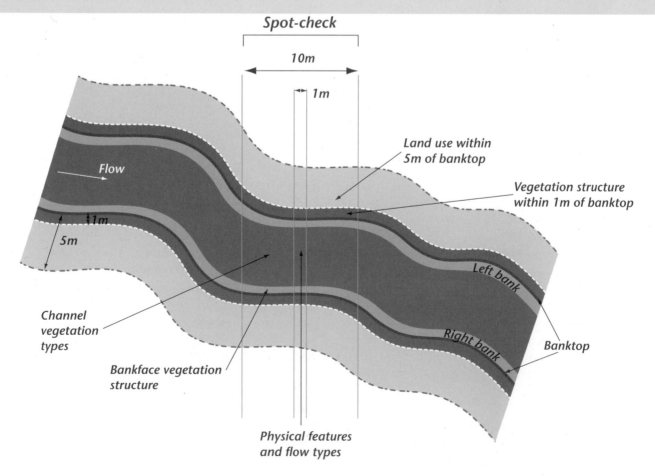

at the spot-checks are recorded (Box 3). Cross-section measurements of water and bankfull width, bank height and water depth are made at one representative location, to provide information about geomorphological processes acting on the channel. The number of riffles, pools and point bars found in the site is also recorded. The attributes recorded by RHS capture the structural variation of rivers relevant to a wide range of organisms, from microscopic algae to fish, birds and mammals.

2.9 RHS can be carried out by a trained and accredited surveyor at any time of the year, but unshaded lowland rivers in southern England often become overgrown with channel and bank vegetation in the late summer. Heavily shaded rivers and those in the uplands containing little or no summer reed-growth are suitable for RHS survey over a much longer season. However, for consistency, the RHS reference sites in England and Wales were surveyed during May and June. In Scotland and Northern Ireland, surveys were carried out over a longer season.

2.10 Variations in channel features, and bank vegetation in particular, were recorded at ten specially selected sites in England during a 12-month period in 1995 - 96, so that RHS survey data collected outside the May to June period could be seasonally calibrated if necessary.

2.11 RHS can be carried out during low flow conditions, but not during high or flood flows because many in-stream features become invisible. More importantly, diagnostic flow types of in-stream habitat features become modified, extended or restricted, making comparative analysis invalid. A special research project is investigating this modified flow behaviour.

Establishing a baseline of RHS reference sites

2.12 An early requirement for RHS was to establish, for England and Wales in the first instance, a geographically representative baseline sample of river habitat features, collected in a consistent and repeatable fashion. This was achieved by surveying a network of reference sites based on a stratified random sample of those rivers classified for water quality purposes. However, the RHS reference sites were selected independently of existing chemical and biological sampling points, because the latter are located in a non-random manner.

2.13 Data from the RHS reference sites now provide a geographically representative baseline

sample of habitat features and impacts associated with rivers and streams classified for water quality throughout the UK and the Isle of Man. As a result, **any** 500m length of river surveyed using RHS can be categorised and its habitat quality assessed, by comparing it with other sites of similar physical character.

2.14 As with other UK-based surveys, the Ordnance Survey 10 x 10 km grid squares were used as a sampling framework[20]. For convenience, however, all coastal squares with less than 50 per cent of land area above high water mark were omitted from the baseline reference site network.

2.15 The original focus for RHS development was England and Wales, and a three-year sampling period was planned. Three individual RHS sites in each of the 1,523 qualifying 10km squares were sampled during 1994 - 96, one in each square in successive years. Given some survey-related difficulties, results from 4,559 sites rather than 4,569 are presented.

2.16 Rivers indicated on 1:250,000 scale topographical maps qualified for inclusion in the network, but tidal reaches and canals were specifically excluded. Sites were selected on the basis of random selection of tetrads (2km x 2km) within each qualifying 10km square. The main qualifying criterion was that the watercourse had been classified for water quality as indicated by the 1985 River Quality Map based on the National Water Council classification[21]. Where no such classified watercourses existed within a 10km square, any watercourse qualified. In the three cases in England where a 10km square did not contain a watercourse shown on the 1:250,000 scale map, the 1:50,000 scale Ordnance Survey map was used to determine site location.

2.17 In 1995, Scotland and Northern Ireland joined the RHS initiative. In Scotland, one site in all but ten of the 779 qualifying squares was sampled over a two-year period, 1995 and 1996. Because some 10km squares were inaccessible by road, site selection had the added practical requirement of being within 2km of a vehicle track. In Northern Ireland, one site in each of 133 qualifying squares was sampled in both 1995 and 1996, giving 266 sites in all. To extend the picture, three RHS sites in each of six qualifying squares on the Isle of Man, were sampled in 1997 (Figure 3).

2.18 For England and Wales, the baseline sample represents 2279 km of watercourse or 6.6 per cent of the total length classified for water quality purposes. The baseline sample in Scotland is 384.5km,

- • One site
- • Two sites
- • Three sites
- × Not sampled

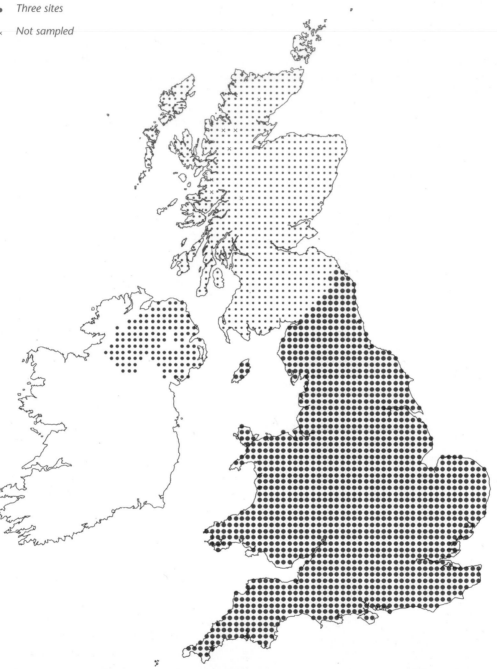

Physically diverse channel structure - River Rawthey, Yorkshire Dales

In-stream habitat structure provided by vegetation - River Ouzel, Buckinghamshire

Wetland margin, adding habitat value to the River Hull, Yorkshire

representing 0.8 per cent of classified river length and that for Northern Ireland 133km, or 5.7 per cent of classified rivers. The total length of rivers classified for water quality in the UK and the Isle of Man is about 85,000km. The baseline survey of RHS reference sites represents a sample of this total length. However, the effectiveness of the sample is not determined by the proportion of the total population it represents, but by the number of samples and the variability of the population. Nevertheless, in considering the results, differences between England and Wales, Scotland and Northern Ireland in terms of RHS sample size, access criteria and the basis of rivers used for water quality classification, must all be borne in mind.

2.19   Map-based and field data from all the reference sites were entered onto the RHS computer database and verified. Data analysis can, therefore, be based on the locational and geographical attributes of a site or sites, as well as any single feature or combination of features on the RHS form (Appendix 1). In addition, slide transparencies of each site, scanned into the database, provide a pictorial archive.

Using RHS to assess habitat quality

2.20   Statistical analysis and professional judgment have been combined to generate habitat quality outputs. Those presented in this Report represent early illustrative attempts. Further analyses and testing will undoubtedly modify and refine the precise details, and updated versions will need to be developed. However, the principles underpinning the current approach should withstand the test of time.

2.21   Analysis of the RHS database allows the physical characteristics of rivers and streams to be compared, and habitat quality to be assessed, either using criteria derived from known conservation interest, or the occurrence of specific features as recorded in the reference network. It should be noted, however, that for an individual site, other measures, such as river water quality class, may differ greatly from this habitat quality assessment, since they describe different attributes.

2.22   Quality can be determined by four broad approaches: (i) a straightforward rule-based separation to identify the very best (outstanding) sites; using habitat features which (ii) singly, or (iii) in combination, are rare; and (iv) a scoring system (Figure 4).

2.23   The basis for assessing habitat quality is:

- evaluation is determined at **site** (500m) level;

- quality is based on the presence of channel and river corridor features which are known to be of **value to wildlife**;

- the two main factors which determine habitat quality are the **diversity** and **'naturalness'** of physical structure;

- the system is calibrated, wherever possible, using known top quality sites surveyed specifically for this purpose *(see 2.41 - 2.44)*.

2.24   In general, habitat and biological diversity in rivers are closely linked. The occurrence and spatial pattern of features such as riffles, pools and point bars are, in a scale-dependent fashion, important in determining the type, distribution and abundance of aquatic wildlife. Other features which provide structure, such as in-stream and bankside vegetation, or trees, also contribute to habitat and biological variety[22]. Where rivers have a floodplain, riparian wetlands indicate that the hydrological links with the river corridor are still intact, thereby adding further value to habitat structure.

Figure 4 Four ways to assess habitat quality using RHS.

	QUESTION	BASIS FOR ANSWER
1	Is the site **outstanding**?	Must have pristine (totally unmodified) channel AND exclusively semi-natural land-use
2	Is the site of high habitat quality based on the occurrence of one or more rare features?	Presence of at least one natural feature which occurs in 5% or less of RHS reference sites within a particular geographical area and/or of the same river type
3	Is the site of high habitat quality based on the occurrence of a rare **combination** of features?	Presence of a combination of natural features which occurs in 5% or less of RHS reference sites within a particular geographical area and/or of the same river type
4	How does the HQA score for the site compare with other sites of the same river type?	Compare it with all HQA scores from RHS reference sites of the same river type, if possible calibrated using a top quality benchmark site

2.25 RHS quality assessment does **not** take account of naturalness in the strictly biological sense. Habitat features are recorded as physical structures, and vegetation categories are recorded irrespective of whether they contain native or non-native species. Examples of established non-native plants would include Canadian pondweed *Elodea canadensis* growing submerged in the channel, Himalayan balsam *Impatiens glandulifera* colonising a bank or point bar, and sycamore *Acer pseudoplatanus* growing as a bankside tree or present in adjacent broadleaf woodland.

Outstanding sites - separating the best from the rest

2.26 Given the priority afforded to naturalness as the primary criterion for wildlife conservation interest, there are two simple rules for identifying an outstanding RHS site: one is that the river channel is pristine, that is, totally free from artificial modification *(see 2.49)*; the second is that land use in the river corridor is entirely semi-natural. Examples of semi-natural land use include broadleaf woodland, native pinewood, peatbog, fen or whatever represents the climax vegetation. Since there are significant regional differences in semi-natural vegetation, outstanding sites need to be confirmed on advice from relevant conservation experts.

2.27 The ability to determine outstanding sites on this basis, regardless of river type, provides a valuable tool for the planning process, enabling the best sites in whatever context to be identified and appropriate protection measures taken.

River type as a basis for comparing habitat quality

2.28 During the initial development of RHS, attempts were made to devise a single, fixed national classification of river types for assessing habitat quality. The eleven preliminary river segment types presented in RHS Report 1 proved unworkable for this specific purpose, but nevertheless provide a useful basis for describing overall river character[23] *(see 5.3)*.

2.29 Given the difficulties in trying to apply a fixed classification of river types to the continuum of natural variation in the physical character of channels, a more practical and flexible approach is required. This means interrogating the RHS database using a set of rules, or selection criteria, to identify those reference sites with the most similar attributes. The criteria chosen will vary, depending on the

purpose of the quality assessment exercise, but may be based on map-derived variables such as altitude, geology, and height of source. If necessary, field-generated measurements such as channel width can also be used (Box 4). The resulting group of sites represents a sample of the 'river type' determined by the selection rules or criteria used. Some descriptive examples appear in Box 5.

2.30 It is important to realise that the more general the selection rules, the less precisely defined the river type will be and, because of the natural variability involved, the lower the confidence for comparing either general characteristics or habitat quality. Stricter selection rules will mean that fewer reference sites will qualify. In Chapter 3, a simplistic 'upland' and 'lowland' classification of all RHS reference sites is used. Chapter 4 illustrates how

Box 4 Some selection criteria for deriving river type.

Primary attributes	Secondary attributes
Solid geology	Above or below tree-line
Drift geology	Planform of channel
Altitude	Distance to on-line lake
Channel slope (gradient)	Valley form
Distance from source	Size (water width, mean discharge)
Height of source	Baseflow index

Box 5 Some descriptive examples of river types.

River type (those with asterisk appear in Chapter 4)	Present in RHS network	Benchmarked for quality
Winterbournes	Very few	Yes
Chalk rivers*	Yes	Yes
Groundwater-fed sandstone rivers	Yes	No
Peatbog streams	Very few	Yes
Steep streams*	Yes	Yes
Upland plateau rivers	Yes	No
Limestone rivers	Very few	Yes
Gorge rivers	Yes	Yes
Coastal streams	Very few	Yes
Mountain valley rivers*	Yes	Yes
Small, lowland riffle-dominated rivers*	Yes	Yes
Clay rivers	Yes	Yes
Inter-lake (lochan) rivers	Yes	Yes
Large lowland rivers	Yes	No
Drains and dykes	Yes	No

habitat quality can be expressed, using four, more tightly defined river types, as examples.

Rarity as a quality measure

2.31   Sites of high habitat quality can be determined using rarity as the primary criterion. This can be applied to the occurrence of a single rare feature of known wildlife value, or to a rare combination of features which individually may not be scarce.

2.32   Regardless of the approach, rarity needs to be based on the occurrence of a feature or a combination of features in the RHS reference site network. Given the significant regional variations in landscape character across the UK and the Isle of Man, it is essential that the geographical context for rarity is explicit. A rare feature in the Midlands of England may be relatively common in Wales or Scotland, but nevertheless deserves special attention when putting site value into a regional or local context.

2.33   Box 6 lists some natural features which qualify as rare by occurring in 5 per cent or less of upland and lowland RHS reference sites overall. Their occurrence individually in England and Wales, Scotland and Northern Ireland is also shown for comparision. Similar lists can be derived for any region of the UK, although as a rule of thumb, at least 100 reference sites are required to make the basis for rarity meaningful.

2.34   Table 1 illustrates how combinations of features can also be used to define rarity for a given river type. In this instance, the percentage occurrence of various combinations of representative features in steep streams is given. This example indicates that, whilst 91.4 per cent of all RHS reference sites of this type have exposed boulders, only 11.0 per cent of sites have the combination of exposed boulders, bedrock, cascades, waterfalls and extensive broadleaf woodland (or native pinewood) on both banks which together are considered special. This approach can be applied to any river type in an overall, regional, or even a local context and is likely to be the most useful day-to-day method for assessing the relative habitat quality of a site.

2.35   An alternative, but similar, approach could be used, with sites only qualifying as high quality if minimum levels for habitat features are met. For example, continuous or semi-continuous trees along both banks and extensive broadleaf woodland could be used as two tree-related quality criteria for identifying how many sites qualify for a particular habitat quality standard.

Box 6 Natural habitat features with an occurrence of 5 per cent or less in upland and lowland RHS reference sites. *Insufficient upland sites surveyed in Northern Ireland for meaningful comparison.*

Feature	UK and Isle of Man		England & Wales		Scotland		Northern Ireland
	upland	lowland	upland	lowland	upland	lowland	lowland
Valley form							
Gorge	✓	✓	✓	✓	✓		✓
Channel features							
Braided/side channels		✓		✓			✓
Waterfalls more than 5m high		✓		✓	✓		✓
Extensive exposed bankside tree roots	✓		✓		✓		✓
Extensive underwater tree roots	✓	✓	✓		✓	✓	✓
Extensive coarse woody debris	✓	✓	✓	✓	✓	✓	✓
Extensive fallen trees	✓	✓	✓	✓	✓	✓	✓
Land use							
Carr	✓	✓	✓	✓	✓	✓	✓
Extensive broadleaf woodland on both banks					✓		
Extensive wetland on both banks	✓	✓	✓	✓	✓		✓

Extensive refers to at least 33% of channel or banklength

Footnote: this is only a selection; other features occur at 5 per cent or less of RHS reference sites, but cannot be considered rare in a wider context.

Habitat Quality Assessment (HQA) score

2.36   Scoring is a blunt instrument for describing any ecological system, especially complex and dynamic systems such as rivers. Whilst it does have its detractors, it provides a useful way for evaluating the relative quality of a site and the potential impact of proposed management. Scoring can be used to quantify (i) improvement or degradation of habitat quality; and (ii) how an anticipated change could affect a particular habitat resource at catchment, regional or national level.

2.37   The habitat quality assessment (HQA) scoring system, described in Appendix 2, is basically a broad measure of the diversity and 'naturalness' of the physical (habitat) structure of a site, including both the channel and river corridor. The HQA score is determined by the presence and extent of habitat features of known wildlife interest recorded during the field survey. Rare features, such as waterfalls more than 5m high and extensive fallen trees, attract additional points.

2.38   The current HQA system has been developed primarily for use in England and Wales. It needs to be tested, refined and adapted to take account of regional variations across the UK. For example, the special quality of pristine rivers and streams occurring in naturally treeless mountain areas above 700m, blanket bogs, coastal machair and other wind-stressed landscapes found in parts of Scotland are not adequately accounted for in the current version.

2.39   Point scoring for the HQA system is based on a consensus of informed professional judgment. It is subjective, but provides the necessary consistency for comparisons. Features that score are consistent with those included in the *System for Evaluating Rivers for Conservation* (SERCON), for which a panel of ecological experts identified the attributes of most value to riverine wildlife[24]. However, given the limitation of scoring, the system may not always identify immediately those sites which have the most extensive or very best examples of habitat features. The HQA score should therefore not be used alone to determine management action.

2.40   Although independent of river type, comparison of individual HQA scores has to involve sites of similar river type, determined in turn by specific selection rules and hence the purpose of the exercise. Comparison of HQA scores across different river types is not meaningful.

Table 1 An example of determining the quality of steep streams, using combinations of habitat features.

Features	Percentage of steep stream RHS reference sites with required attributes *(n = 336)*
exposed boulders	91.4
exposed boulders, bedrock	67.9
exposed boulders, bedrock & cascades	64.3
exposed boulders, bedrock, cascades & waterfall(s)	32.7
exposed boulders, bedrock, cascades, waterfall(s), & extensive moorland/heath on both banks	11.9
exposed boulders, bedrock, cascades, waterfall(s), & extensive broadleaf woodland on both banks	11.0

A steep stream in Beinn Eighe NNR, Wester Ross, with a combination of bedrock, exposed boulders, cascades and extensive woodland

Calibration, using top quality sites

2.41 During 1994, the first survey year, it became clear that very few reference sites in England and Wales had a combination of totally unmodified channels and an extensive semi-natural landscape. Anticipating that some of the very best sections of river would not be included in the baseline survey of RHS reference sites, it was decided to establish a 'top quality' series of benchmark sites by specially surveying additional rivers of known high wildlife importance in England, Wales and Scotland. Some benchmark sites were also located in the Republic of Ireland (Figure 5).

2.42 Most of the benchmark sites were selected for survey because existing information confirmed their high nature conservation value in terms of plant or animal communities, although this did not always mean that the river habitat was of high value. Other benchmark sites, particularly in lowland England, needed to be traced using map-based information as a preliminary guide.

2.43 In addition to an RHS survey, each benchmark site has had a full macrophyte survey completed and water chemistry analysed. These data and HQA scores are included as a special benchmark section in the RHS database and provide a quality marker for certain river types. Consequently, full calibration of HQA scores is only possible for those river types which include one or more benchmark sites.

2.44 It was remarkably difficult to find 500m lengths of river in the lowlands which were suitable for benchmarking in the strictest sense. Such is the extent of human influence in the UK, that there are hardly any pristine 500m lengths of large lowland river flowing through a semi-natural landscape. Some benchmarks are therefore some way short of natural, but they nevertheless represent high habitat quality in the context of the structural degradation of particular river types.

Figure 5 The location of RHS benchmark sites, on a 10km square basis.

River Unshin in County Sligo - a benchmark site for floating reed-mats along the channel margins

River Spey at Speymouth - a large unconstrained river flowing through semi-natural, lowland floodplain forest

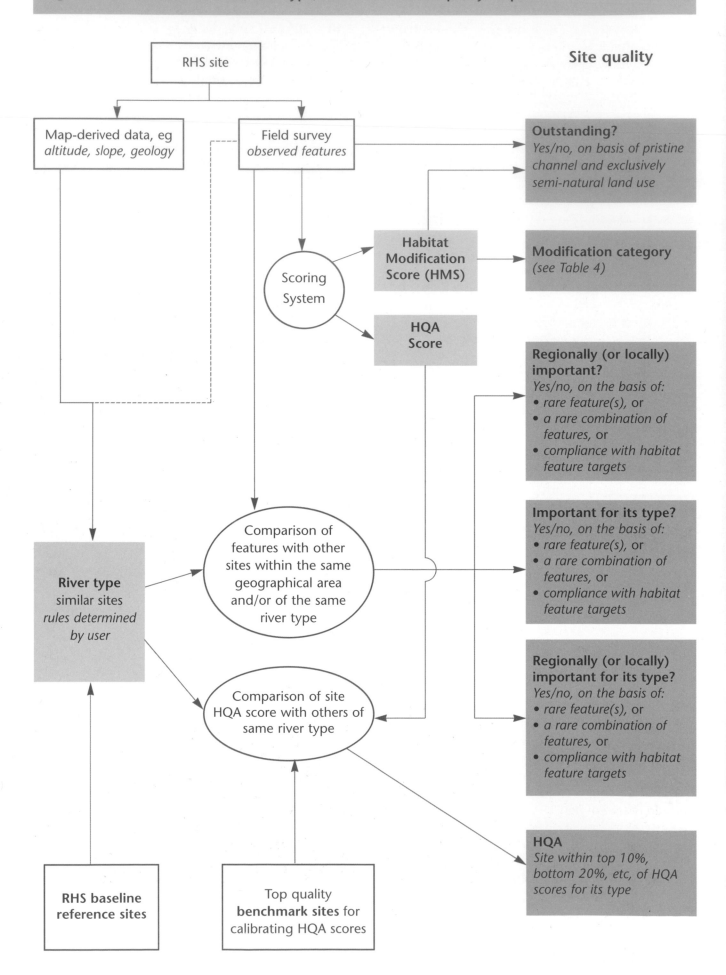

Figure 6 The links between site, river type, scores and habitat quality outputs.

Site quality

RHS site

Map-derived data, eg *altitude, slope, geology*

Field survey *observed features*

Scoring System

Habitat Modification Score (HMS)

HQA Score

River type similar sites *rules determined by user*

Comparison of features with other sites within the same geographical area and/or of the same river type

Comparison of site HQA score with others of same river type

RHS baseline reference sites

Top quality **benchmark sites** for calibrating HQA scores

Outstanding? *Yes/no, on basis of pristine channel and exclusively semi-natural land use*

Modification category *(see Table 4)*

Regionally (or locally) important? *Yes/no, on the basis of:*
- *rare feature(s), or*
- *a rare combination of features, or*
- *compliance with habitat feature targets*

Important for its type? *Yes/no, on the basis of:*
- *rare feature(s), or*
- *a rare combination of features, or*
- *compliance with habitat feature targets*

Regionally (or locally) important for its type? *Yes/no, on the basis of:*
- *rare feature(s), or*
- *a rare combination of features, or*
- *compliance with habitat feature targets*

HQA *Site within top 10%, bottom 20%, etc, of HQA scores for its type*

Classifying habitat quality

2.45   Many management decisions require that the quality of sites is classified. The links between RHS site, river type, HQA scores and outputs are illustrated in Figure 6. River habitat quality is classified in response to specific questions, such as:

- is the site outstanding?

- is the site important within a specified geographical context due to one or more rare features, or a rare combination of features?

- how do features in the site, such as the number of riffles or extent of trees, compare with other sites of the same river type?

- how does the site HQA score compare with others of similar type, and with top quality benchmark examples?

2.46   Classification of habitat quality using RHS is the grouping of sites with similar attributes or scores. Great care is needed when categorising sites as 'excellent', 'good', 'fair' or 'bad' and this approach, used for describing water quality, is helpful **only** for reporting purposes and informing broad management policies. As a general rule, habitat quality assessment, however generated, should be used in conjunction with other available information such as species data if the wider conservation value of a site needs to be determined. This is the basis for using RHS data to help evaluate the overall conservation interest of rivers through the SERCON system[24].

Using RHS to assess artificial channel modification

2.47   River habitat quality is strongly influenced by the type and extent of artificial modification. The three main types affecting river channels are: **reinforcement** (revetment in the form of concrete, steel piling, gabion, rip-rap, etc); **resectioning** (reprofiling through dredging of the bed and banks); and **regulation** of flow by impounding structures. The impact of these modifications may well influence the occurrence of habitat features for a considerable distance downstream or, in the case of major impoundments, upstream as well.

Habitat Modification Score

2.48   By applying a simple set of rules to RHS data, artificial modification to the physical structure of the channel can be expressed as a Habitat Modification Score (HMS). Like the HQA score, the system is an objective application of a set of subjective rules, and is necessary for consistent comparison between sites. It can also be used at a site level to audit predicted or actual impacts resulting from channel works. Points scored are based on the relative impact of modification on habitat features. By assigning a score of 1 to each spot-check entry for resectioning, 2 for reinforcement and allowing for other types of modification, such as weirs, to be accounted for as well, a cumulative HMS score can be used to summarise the severity and extent of structural alteration to the channel (Appendix 3).

2.49   Using the HMS system, sites with a pristine channel, that is, having **no** artificial modification, score zero. Semi-natural channels score a maximum of 2, while the most heavily and extensively modified channels score 45 or more (Box 7). The HMS score is independent of river type, so it can be used to describe artificial modification to physical structure across the board. However, biological factors such as the presence of non-native plant species are not included in the scoring system.

Box 7 Habitat modification score (HMS) categories for describing the physical state of the river channel at RHS sites.	
HMS Score	**Descriptive category of channel**
0	*Pristine*
0 - 2	Semi-natural
3 - 8	Predominantly unmodified
9 - 20	Obviously modified
21 - 44	Significantly modified
45 or more	Severely modified
Footnote: semi-natural includes pristine channels	

2.50   In describing individual RHS sites, both the HQA and HMS scores should be used in conjunction, as together they can give a broad indication of how overall habitat quality and structural modification to the channel might be linked. It is important to bear in mind, however, that the HMS score relates only to modification of the **channel**, while the HQA score is derived from features in the channel **and** the river corridor. The importance of this difference when interpreting results is highlighted in Chapter 4 *(see 4.21).*

Presentation and status of results

2.51 The results presented in Chapters 3 - 5 illustrate different ways of using information derived from the RHS database. They demonstrate how information can be generated to establish the geographical occurrence of specific habitat features, or to confirm which sites are of the most similar physical character or quality. The examples used indicate the analytical capacity of the RHS database. A comprehensive description of ordination techniques to determine site character can be found elsewhere for those who wish to understand the statistical basis for RHS analysis[25].

The lower Rother, East Sussex - a heavily modified lowland river, constrained by floodbanks and managed for flood defence

2.52 In reality, the RHS reference sites are not isolated 500m lengths or river, but nodes linked together within a catchment. It is the analysis of these links, to provide a better understanding of river dynamics and responses to channel modifications and wider catchment use, which has yet to be explored in detail. For the present purpose, the need to establish and report on a habitat quality system generated from individual site data has determined the contents of this Report.

2.53 The results in this Report and accompanying summary fact-sheet need to be viewed with two sources of uncertainty in mind: (i) the observational accuracy of different RHS surveyors, and (ii) the current verification limitations of the RHS database. The first uncertainty has been minimised by training and accreditation controls *(see 2.5)*. Secondly, the process of validating the database has involved double-entry and cross checking for errors. Inevitably, some errors will have been missed, but continuing checks will help to ensure it is fully validated and updated. If results in this Report are to be used for other than broad reporting purposes, the data should be checked with the Environment Agency, SEPA or the Environment and Heritage Service as appropriate.

2.54 As a matter of principle and courtesy, precise locational details of individual RHS sites will not be divulged without the permission of the appropriate riparian landowner(s).

Chapter 3 The physical character of rivers and streams - an overview

Background

3.1   The results in this Chapter, most notably Tables 2, 3 and 4 and also the summary fact-sheet, are presented for the UK and the Isle of Man as a whole **and** separately for England and Wales, Scotland, and Northern Ireland. This simply reflects the administrative responsibilities of the Environment Agency, Scottish Environment Protection Agency (SEPA) and the Environment and Heritage Service, Northern Ireland. RHS data can be tailored for regional, county level, or catchment purposes, but this Report concentrates on providing an overview.

3.2   To avoid over-generalising at the country-level, and to reflect the most important factors determining the physical character of rivers, the data are split into *upland* and *lowland* for more meaningful comparison. Defining upland and lowland has inherent difficulties, but for the purposes of this Report, land more than 200m above sea-level, located north and west of a line joining Start Point in South Devon and Flamborough Head in Yorkshire, has been used to define 'upland'. The remaining areas, including all land south-east of the Start Point - Flamborough Head line, are defined as 'lowland'. This landscape-based division means that 'upland' includes virtually all areas of the UK with an annual rainfall exceeding 1,000mm.

3.3   The bulk of results are presented as pie charts, bar charts and 10km grid square distribution maps. Wherever possible, examples are illustrated by photographs. Unless stated otherwise, results relate to the entire baseline survey of RHS reference sites undertaken during 1994 - 1997 in the UK and the Isle of Man. Only four sites surveyed in Northern Ireland qualified as 'upland' and because this is too few for meaningful comparison, they are omitted from Tables 2, 3 and 4. They are, however, included in the upland total for the UK and Isle of Man. Upland and lowland data from the Isle of Man are included only in the overall total, for similar reasons.

3.4   The differing number of RHS reference sites sampled per 10km square in England and Wales, Scotland and Northern Ireland (Figure 3) has made presentation of the results difficult. Distribution maps are presented as the occurrence (presence or absence) of selected features or combination of features on a 10km square basis across the whole of the UK and the Isle of Man. There is an inherent bias in this approach, given the differing sampling effort in England and Wales compared with Scotland and Northern Ireland. In reality, this bias is not so great, given the representative nature of the sample, so data from all RHS reference sites have been used to provide a full picture at the individual country level.

3.5   Bearing in mind the effects of different sampling effort in England and Wales, Scotland and Northern Ireland, the RHS reference site network can be considered to be a geographically representative cross-section of rivers and streams classified for water quality purposes. This means that the occurrence of habitat features and impacts in the RHS reference network, such as those illustrated in this Chapter, should be indicative of the 85,000km length of rivers and streams shown on 1:250,000 scale maps and classified for water quality.

3.6   A single, summary overview of the physical character of rivers and streams in the UK and the Isle of Man is virtually impossible. However, by concentrating on the landscape scale, specific features can be selected to illustrate general habitat characteristics and major impacts. This Chapter describes the distribution of some of these features and impacts, and concludes with a more specific look at a particular component of physical structure - trees and other riparian vegetation.

General habitat characteristics

3.7   The channels of RHS reference sites range in size from small streams with a water width of less than 1.0m, to large rivers more than 100m across (Figure 7a). There is no recognised definition of when a river becomes a stream, or *vice versa*. Indeed, there is no real advantage in trying to categorise channels

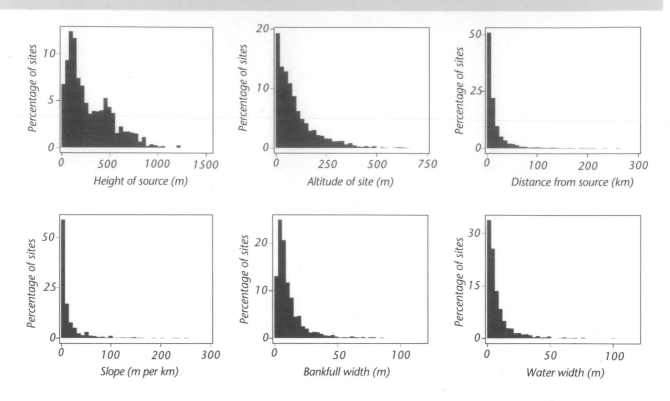

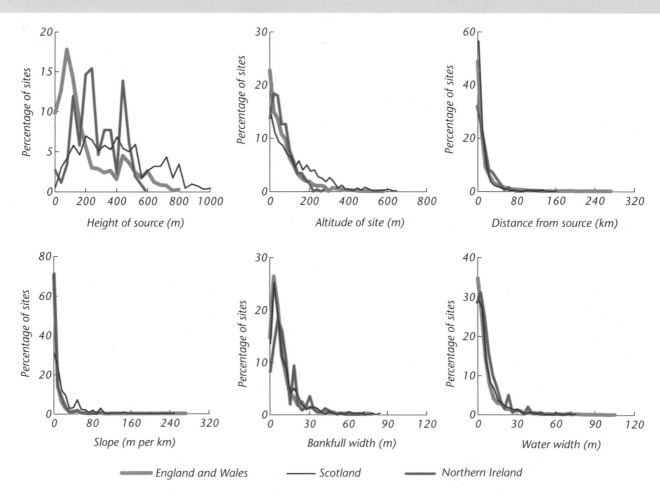

England and Wales　　　Scotland　　　Northern Ireland

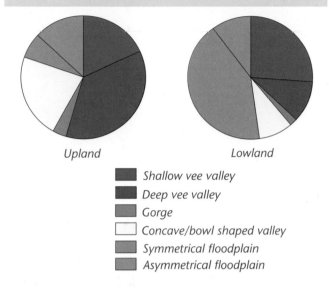

Figure 8 Predominant valley shape at upland and lowland RHS reference sites. *1995 and 1996 data.*

Upland   Lowland

- ◼ Shallow vee valley
- ◼ Deep vee valley
- ◼ Gorge
- ◻ Concave/bowl shaped valley
- ◼ Symmetrical floodplain
- ◼ Asymmetrical floodplain

Figure 9 Flow-related features which occur extensively at upland and lowland RHS reference sites. *1996 data.*

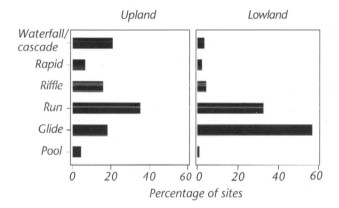

Percentage of sites

Figure 10 Predominant river-bed materials which occur extensively at upland and lowland RHS reference sites.

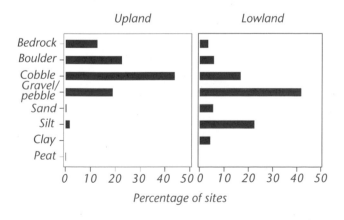

Percentage of sites

on this basis. On Ordnance Survey 1:50,000 scale maps, watercourses less than 5m wide are shown as a single blue line. If, for the purposes of this Chapter, a water width of 5m is taken to be the division between 'rivers' and 'streams', then 51.9 per cent of RHS sites can be classified as 'streams'. Using this rule, the RHS reference site network contains a sample ratio of 6.5 per cent upland streams, 45.4 per cent lowland streams, 4.2 per cent upland rivers and 43.9 per cent lowland rivers.

3.8 The pattern of channel slope (gradient), altitude and height of source all broadly reflect the topography of the UK and Isle of Man, with subtle, but predictable differences between the different countries (Figures 7a and b). The altitude of Northern Ireland RHS reference sites is significantly affected by the river network used for reporting water quality; consequently, only four reference sites are upland.

3.9 Predominant valley shape and flow-related habitats together provide useful indicators of overall character (Figures 8 and 9). In turn, these energy-related factors help to determine the type of predominant bed material (Figure 10). The bed material and flow characteristics, in turn, help to determine which aquatic plants grow in the channel.

3.10 A common perception is that the cool, high energy environment and low nutrient levels in upland streams and rivers mean that they support a different variety of aquatic plants to the warmer, less turbulent waters and higher nutrient levels in lowland channels. This is not reflected in the number of different in-stream channel vegetation types recorded at upland and lowland RHS reference sites (Figure 11). However, in considering individual types, the occurrence of liverworts and mosses contrasts

Figure 11 The number of in-stream channel vegetation types recorded at upland and lowland RHS reference sites.

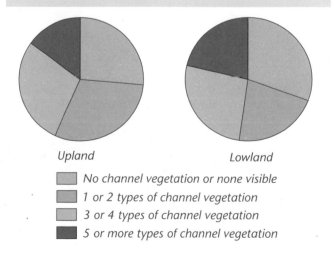

Upland   Lowland

- ◼ No channel vegetation or none visible
- ◼ 1 or 2 types of channel vegetation
- ◼ 3 or 4 types of channel vegetation
- ◼ 5 or more types of channel vegetation

markedly between upland and lowland sites (Figure 12) . Identification of plants to species level would undoubtedly reveal greater differences[26]. The main point is that, regardless of altitude, aquatic plants can provide an important habitat for invertebrates and fish, especially in rivers where otherwise the in-stream channel structure is relatively poor.

An overview of major impacts

3.11   The main driving force behind modifications to river habitats is land management, both historical and current. There are significant differences in predominant land-use recorded at RHS reference sites in England and Wales, Scotland and Northern Ireland (Figure 13). In many areas, constraints imposed by urban development are largely irreversible.

3.12   Present-day tree cover is a good reflection of the impact of land-use change. Apart from the naturally treeless blanket bog areas of Scotland and Northern Ireland, the summits of the Cairngorms and other high mountains, and the windswept Scottish Western and Northern Isles, the natural vegetation of the UK and the Isle of Man would be predominantly woodland[13]. England was heavily wooded until the Norman conquest, whilst major deforestation was still occurring in Scotland as recently as the 18th century. Today only 1.4 per cent of Great Britain is covered by ancient semi-natural woodland, and of this 84 per cent is fragmented into areas of less than 21 ha[27]. In Scotland, only 16,000 ha of native pinewood remains[13].

3.13   Where trees can thrive naturally, they are important in determining river habitat quality because they provide shelter, shading, leaf litter input and bank stability. Extensive overhanging boughs, fallen trees, coarse woody debris, debris dams and exposed tree roots provide 'wild' character and highly valued habitat diversity in rivers. However, these features, together with carr woodland, occur extensively only in relatively few RHS reference sites, presumably because of channel management for land

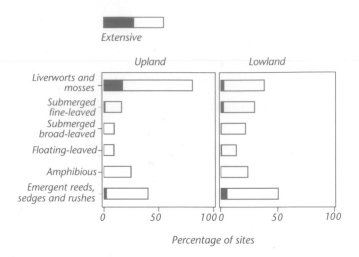

Figure 12 In-stream channel vegetation types occurring in upland and lowland RHS reference sites.

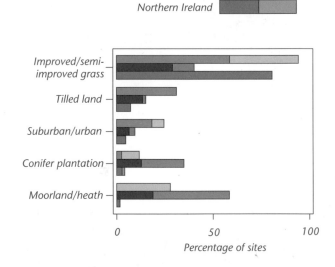

Figure 13 Selected types of land use which occur extensively at upland and lowland RHS reference sites in England and Wales, Scotland and Northern Ireland.

A naturally treeless landscape, Caithness

Coarse woody debris

Carr - a rare riverside habitat

drainage, flood defence, and in some instances, fisheries management purposes (Table 2).

3.14 In the RHS reference network as a whole, artificial modification to the river channel means that only 28.2 per cent of lowland RHS reference sites in England and Wales, 44.3 per cent in Scotland and 20.9 per cent in Northern Ireland can be classified as having a semi-natural physical structure. The occurrence of pristine channel structure is even less (Table 3). In general, the degree of modification is less in upland RHS reference sites (Figure 14). Within upland and lowland categories themselves, the pattern of modification does not vary much with channel width, indicating that small streams are equally as likely to be modified as larger rivers (Figure 15).

3.15 In many instances, more than one type of modification occurs within a site, indicating the different management pressures acting on the river channel, particularly in lowland areas (Figure 16). The main types of modification and their occurrence at RHS reference sites are shown in Table 4, on page 26. Although most involve direct modification to the river channel, others, such as excessive poaching of banks by livestock, may arise from management practices on adjacent land. Catchment-wide problems associated with water quantity and quality can also have an impact on the physical structure of the river channel.

Table 2 The occurrence of some tree-related features at upland and lowland RHS reference sites. *Insufficient upland sites surveyed in Northern Ireland for meaningful comparison.*

	Occurrence as a percentage of RHS reference sites						
Feature	UK and Isle of Man		England & Wales		Scotland		Northern Ireland
	upland	lowland	upland	lowland	upland	lowland	lowland
Extensive shading of channel	23.1	36.8	27.5	38.4	14.3	29.7	53.9
Extensive overhanging boughs	7.4	14.2	9.4	14.3	3.3	17.1	7.0
Exposed bankside tree roots*	38.0	49.7	42.3	50.4	30.2	46.5	48.8
Extensive exposed bankside tree roots	2.2	6.0	2.5	6.1	1.6	6.8	4.3
Underwater tree roots*	23.4	24.8	30.2	56.5	9.3	25.1	32.9
Extensive underwater tree roots	1.2	4.9	1.5	5.7	0.5	1.2	1.2
Fallen trees*	31.1	36.8	34.4	36.8	24.7	37.2	35.7
Extensive fallen trees	1.5	1.3	1.2	1.3	2.2	1.5	0.0
Coarse woody debris*	35.7	51.6	42.3	52.7	22.5	43.8	52.3
Extensive coarse woody debris	1.9	3.1	2.0	3.4	1.6	2.7	0.4
Debris dams *(1995 and 1996 only)*	17.0	18.6	22.0	21.0	9.9	11.0	12.0
Carr	1.3	3.5	1.9	3.6	0.5	1.9	3.5
Number of sites	593	5019	404	4155	181	588	262

* present and extensive occurrence combined   *Extensive means at least a third of the channel*

Table 3 The extent of artificial channel modification at upland and lowland RHS reference sites, expressed as HMS category. *Insufficient upland sites surveyed in Northern Ireland for meaningful comparison.*

	Occurrence as a percentage of RHS reference sites						
HMS score and category	UK and Isle of Man		England & Wales		Scotland		Northern Ireland
	upland	lowland	upland	lowland	upland	lowland	lowland
Pristine (0)	*41.8*	*15.1*	*38.9*	*13.6*	*47.3*	*28.0*	*10.1*
Semi-natural (0 - 2)	61.4	29.7	56.9	28.2	70.9	44.3	20.9
Predominantly unmodified (3 - 8)	22.9	21.3	26.0	20.9	16.5	23.8	20.9
Obviously modified (9 - 20)	11.6	20.6	12.1	21.3	10.4	15.1	20.5
Significantly modified (21 - 44)	3.2	24.8	4.0	25.7	1.6	14.9	32.6
Severely modified (45+)	0.7	3.5	1.0	3.7	0.0	1.7	5.0
Number of sites	593	5019	404	4155	181	588	262

Figure 14 Habitat modification at upland and lowland RHS reference sites in England and Wales, Scotland and Northern Ireland.

Figure 15 The relationship between habitat modification score and channel size at upland and lowland RHS reference sites.

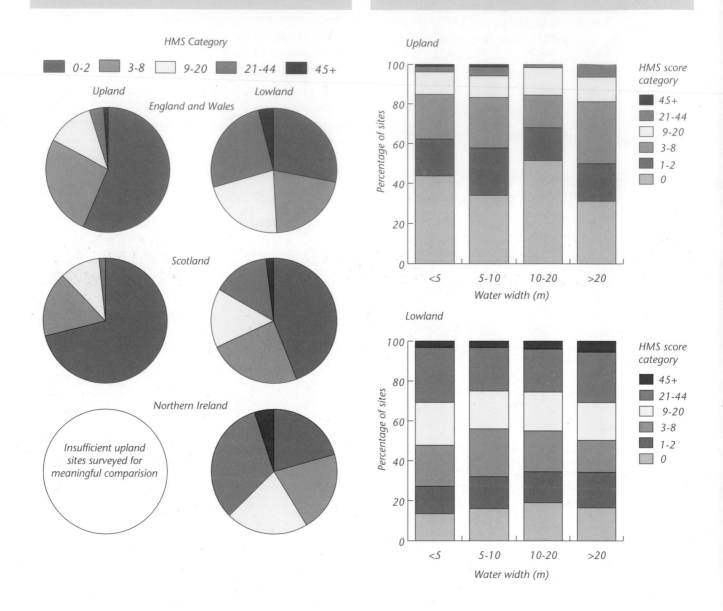

Figure 16 The number of different types of channel modification at upland and lowland RHS reference sites.

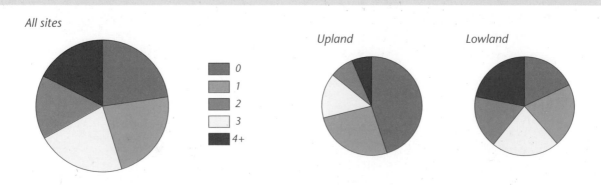

Direct modifications

3.16 Land drainage and flood defence have had a major impact on the structure of many lowland channels. Overall, more than 30 per cent of lowland RHS reference sites have extensively resectioned banks, whilst 10.7 per cent have extensive embankments (Table 4; Figures 17 and 18). Some channels are entirely artifical, such as the drainage dykes of the East Anglian Fens and Somerset Levels.

3.17 The distribution of RHS reference sites with extensively reinforced banks is closely associated with that of urban areas, major transport routes and river

navigations which need to be provided with strong protection against erosion (Figure 19). Overall, 4.9 per cent of upland and 11.2 per cent of lowland reference sites have extensive bank reinforcement (Table 4). The impact of urban land use on river banks is further illustrated by comparing the occurrence of various materials used for hard bank reinforcement at RHS reference sites in urban and other settings (Figure 20).

3.18 Impoundment of river channels by weirs or sluices is widespread, with one or more impounding structures present in 8.4 per cent of upland and 15.0 per cent of lowland RHS reference sites (Table 4).

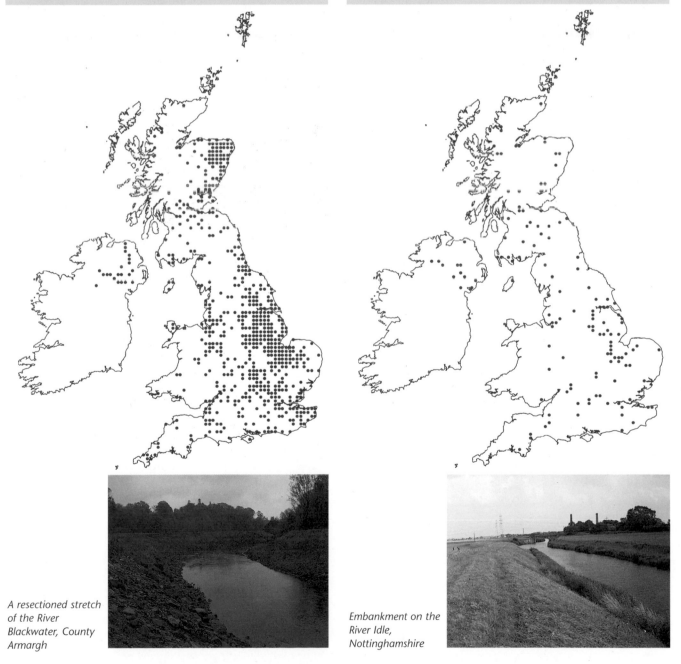

Figure 17 The occurrence of extensive bank resectioning at RHS reference sites, on a 10km square basis.

Figure 18 The occurrence of extensive embankments at RHS reference sites, on a 10km square basis.

A resectioned stretch of the River Blackwater, County Armargh

Embankment on the River Idle, Nottinghamshire

Table 4 The occurrence of selected modifying factors at upland and lowland RHS reference sites.
Insufficient upland sites surveyed in Northern Ireland for meaningful comparison.

Modifying factor	Occurrence as a percentage of RHS reference sites						
	UK and Isle of Man		England & Wales		Scotland		Northern Ireland
	upland	lowland	upland	lowland	upland	lowland	lowland
Channel straightening	0.0	6.2	0.0	7.3	0.0	0.5	0.4
Bank resectioning*	12.5	44.0	10.1	45.6	17.0	32.1	53.5
Extensive bank resectioning	4.9	31.8	3.7	33.2	7.7	19.4	36.8
Bank reinforcement*	35.4	51.9	41.6	52.0	23.1	44.8	66.3
Extensive bank reinforcement	4.9	11.2	6.2	11.3	2.2	7.1	18.6
Embankments*	5.1	14.9	5.2	14.3	4.4	12.1	31.0
Extensive embankments	2.7	10.7	2.7	11.0	2.7	7.6	11.2
Weir(s) or sluices	8.4	15.0	10.6	15.6	3.3	8.5	19.8
Culvert(s)	3.5	9.3	5.2	10.5	0.0	4.8	3.1
Bridge(s)	27.8	43.3	28.2	45.1	27.5	37.0	29.1
Ford(s)	6.4	3.6	6.2	3.2	6.6	6.6	4.3
Extensively poached banks	1.7	2.7	2.0	3.0	1.1	1.7	12.8
Number of sites	593	5019	404	4155	181	588	262

* present and extensive occurrence combined *Extensive means at least a third of one or both banks*

Figure 19 The occurrence of extensive bank reinforcement at RHS reference sites, on a 10km square basis.

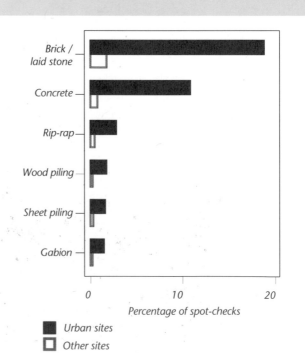

Heavily reinforced river channels

Figure 20 A comparison of reinforcement materials used along banks in urban and other RHS reference sites.

Brick / laid stone
Concrete
Rip-rap
Wood piling
Sheet piling
Gabion

Percentage of spot-checks
0 10 20

■ Urban sites
□ Other sites

Weirs - found frequently at lowland sites

A flow-gauging weir

Figure 21 **The occurrence of weirs at RHS reference sites, on a 10km square basis.**

○ *1 weir*
● *2 or more weirs*

Weirs are particularly prevalent at RHS reference sites in lowland England and Northern Ireland (Figure 21).

3.19   Culverts are often closely associated with urban areas and major transport links. Indeed, in many urban areas rivers and streams have been historically culverted and pass unnoticed below the streets[28]. Since they are not shown on current maps, this significant localised impact was not recorded by the baseline RHS survey and therefore tempers the results. Nevertheless, the 9.3 per cent occurrence of culverts at lowland RHS reference sites is suprisingly high, although as expected, the majority are found in England and Wales (Table 4; Figure 22).

Figure 22 **The occurrence of culverts at RHS reference sites, on a 10km square basis.**

○ *One culvert*
● *2 or more culverts*

A culvert

27

3.20 The occurrence of bridge crossings reflects the high density of the footpath network and transport links, particularly in lowland England and Wales where 15.5 per cent of RHS reference sites have two or more bridges (Table 4; Figure 23).

Indirect modifications

3.21 Poaching of river banks by livestock can be beneficial in small quantities because it produces a specific waterside habitat important for certain annual plant species. Extensive poaching, however, can destabilise the bank, leading to channel overwidening and silt release. Poached banks were recorded at 21.7 per cent of RHS reference sites with predominantly pasture land use, and poaching was extensive at a fifth of these.

3.22 Siltation in the channel is a natural process, but can be exacerbated by river or catchment management practices which promote gullying and erosion. Excessive siltation can cause significant problems by smothering trout and salmon spawning gravels, and in lowland sites, by promoting excessive reed growth. It was noted by surveyors as an impact in 0.8 per cent of upland and 1.9 per cent of lowland RHS reference sites.

Figure 24 The occurrence of completely dry RHS reference sites, on a 10km square basis.

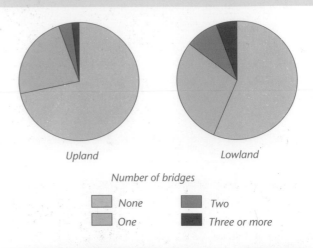

Figure 23 The proportion of upland and lowland RHS reference sites with bridges.

Upland   *Lowland*

Number of bridges

- None
- One
- Two
- Three or more

A heavily poached bank

A seasonally dry river channel - Inchnadamph NNR, Highland Region

Extensive floodplain wetlands such as this relict fritillary meadow at Cricklade, Wiltshire, are now rare.

Figure 25 The occurrence of natural and artificial open water alongside RHS reference sites, on a 10km square basis.

○ Natural
• Artificial

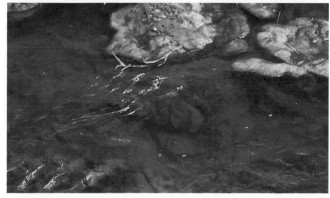

Artifical open water - a recently created riverside fishing pond

Filamentous algae smothering the river-bed

Wetlands and hydrological issues

3.23   Many headwaters which flow only as a result of winter rains, or following good groundwater recharge, dry up for extended periods during drought. In parts of central, north-east and eastern England, the period November 1995 to May 1997 was the driest period for more than 250 years. It is not surprising, therefore, that a number of RHS reference sites visited were dry (Figure 24), although the relative impact of drought and over-abstraction is not known. In limestone areas, there are streams which disappear naturally below ground every summer, leaving a dry channel. These are relatively rare and therefore of special interest.

3.24   The historical loss of floodplain wetlands is well documented[29]. In a natural state and with semi-natural land use, most lowland rivers with a floodplain would have extensive wetland associated with them. It is testament to the efficiency of measures taken to improve agricultural output in the lowlands that only 4.2 per cent of RHS reference sites below 50m altitude, and with a symmetrical or asymmetrical floodplain valley form, have extensive wetland recorded alongside one or both banks.

3.25   The same pattern is evident regarding the relatively rare occurrence of natural open water, including backwaters and abandoned ox-bow channels, in the river corridor. Indeed, artificial open waters such as fishing lakes and gravel pits, many of which have been created in the recent past, are more widespread than natural open water features alongside RHS reference sites in England and Wales (Figure 25).

Eutrophication

3.26   Nutrient enrichment of water is another factor which can influence river habitats, because it can affect the type and abundance of in-stream channel vegetation and hence the habitat available to aquatic animal life. This process of enrichment, together with the biological changes it causes, is known as eutrophication. Excessive nutrient input encourages the growth of filamentous green algae such as *Cladophora* and *Enteromorpha* which can smother other plants, limit their growth or eradicate them altogether. The 11.4 and 11.0 per cent occurrence of extensive algal growth in upland and lowland RHS reference sites respectively, may have some link with eutrophication, but as some filamentous algae can be abundant in nutrient poor waters, this hypothesis needs further analysis.

Trees and riparian vegetation

3.27 For many areas, particularly in the intensively farmed countryside, riverside trees are significant features of the landscape, because they provide important structural diversity. Semi-continuous or continuous tree cover is found along one bank in 7.2 per cent of upland and 19.1 per cent of lowland RHS reference sites, and along both banks in 26.8 per cent of upland and 36.5 per cent of lowland RHS reference sites. The association between this amount of tree cover and predominant adjacent land use is shown in Figure 26.

3.28 Despite the importance of riverside trees to the landscape as a whole, the lack of trees is significant in certain areas (Figure 27). Grazing pressure by sheep and deer in upland areas can prevent tree growth, except in inaccessible gorge reaches, and 28.9 per cent of upland RHS reference sites in mainland Great Britain below 700m altitude are treeless. However, in some lowland parts of north-west Scotland and the Isles, a combination of climatic and soil conditions prevents tree growth.

Figure 26 Predominant land use along banks with semi-continuous or continuous tree cover at RHS reference sites.

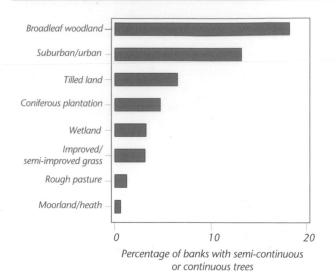

Percentage of banks with semi-continuous or continuous trees

Figure 27 The occurrence of upland and lowland RHS reference sites without trees, on a 10km square basis.

- Upland
- Lowland

Riverside trees as a landscape feature

Glen Roy, Highland Region

A Cotswold valley

Figure 28 The occurrence of RHS reference sites with a weed-choked channel, on a 10km square basis.

3.29 In lowland areas with extensive tilled land on both banks, 15.0 per cent of RHS reference sites are treeless. The absence of trees not only impoverishes the landscape and river habitat, but the lack of shading can also promote the prodigious growth of reeds and other macrophytes which may choke small lowland watercourses (Figure 28).

3.30 Riparian vegetation structure contributes significantly to the wider landscape and to the conservation value of rivers in areas of intensive agriculture. Both the extent and the structure of riparian vegetation help provide a wildlife refuge corridor. Simple or complex banktop vegetation structure provided by herbs, shrubs and trees occurs extensively along 47.4 per cent of banks next to predominantly tilled land, compared with 86.5 per cent along banks with a predominantly broadleaf woodland setting. This association between adjacent land use and banktop vegetation structure can be determined even more clearly, using spot-check information (Figure 29).

Figure 29 Banktop vegetation structure associated with four types of immediately adjacent land use. *Spot-check data.*

A reed-choked lowland channel

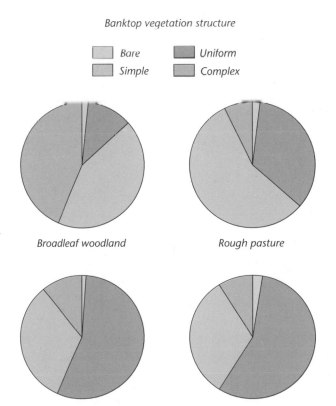

Banktop vegetation structure

- Bare
- Simple
- Uniform
- Complex

Broadleaf woodland *Rough pasture*

Improved grassland *Tilled land*

Riparian wildlife corridor between the channel and tilled farmland

3.31   Agri-environment incentive schemes such as the Habitat Scheme (Water Fringe Option), Countryside Stewardship, Tir Cymen and Scottish Countryside Premium Scheme, aim to encourage farmers to manage their riverside land to provide refuges for wildlife. They represent a good opportunity to restore lost wildlife habitat, reversing the habitat fragmentation of the past.

3.32   Urban landscapes can also benefit from the effect of wildlife corridors provided by rivers, with trees and other riparian vegetation contributing much valued diversity to a predominantly built-up landscape (Figure 26).

Bankside trees enhancing the urban setting of the River Avon, Bath

Conifers alongside the River Esk, south-west Scotland

3.33   Commercial planting of conifers has had a major impact on many upland landscapes, particularly in Wales and Scotland. This is reflected in the occurrence of extensive coniferous plantations along one or both banks at 13.3 per cent of upland RHS reference sites. The planting and felling of these conifers can have a significant impact on water quality and quantity, although recent improvements in forestry management have helped to reduce these effects[30].

Riverside alders

3.34   In many areas, native alders are an important feature of the river landscape. They provide bank stability, and a source of food and shelter for insects, mammals and birds. Their intricate network of underwater roots also provides an important refuge for aquatic invertebrates and fish fry. There has never been a national census of riverside alders in Britain, probably because they have always been taken for granted. In 1993, however, some alders in south-east England were found to be suffering from a disease caused by the fungus *Phytophthora*. It was only then that concerns arose that riparian alder loss could potentially occur on a scale similar to that caused by Dutch Elm disease. This would have a profound impact on landscape, wildlife and river bank stability where riverside alders are abundant.

3.35   By recording healthy alders and those suspected of being diseased at RHS reference sites (Figure 30) and referring to Forestry Commission data, both the distribution of riverside alders and the incidence of Phytophthora disease is now better understood. Not all alders along the same reach of river are affected to the same extent and it appears that some trees are resistant[31]. Research by the Forestry Commission is currently exploring how to contain the spread of the disease.

Invasive alien bankside weeds

3.36   The extensive network of river corridors provides for the easy passage of waterborne seeds and uprooted plants. Many native aquatic and waterside plants take advantage of this to propagate. By the same token, rivers are highly vulnerable to colonisation by invasive alien plants established through accidental or deliberate introduction. A number of such plants have proliferated in this way[32].

3.37   Giant hogweed poses a public health hazard because, on contact, its sap will cause a skin rash in the presence of sunlight. Japanese knotweed spreads by rhizomes and forms dense thickets which can

Figure 30 The occurrence of alders, including those suspected of having Phytophthora disease, at RHS reference sites, on a 10km square basis.

○ Alders present (1996)

● Diseased alders present (1995 &1996)

▦ Complete data unavailable for healthy alders

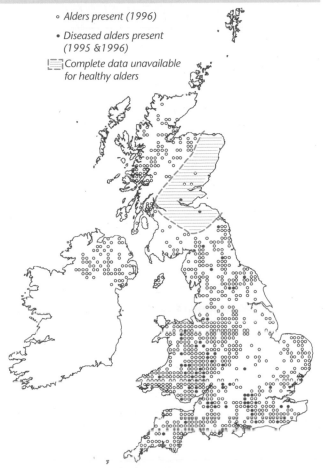

Diseased riverside alders

Underwater roots of alder

Figure 31 The occurrence of giant hogweed at RHS reference sites, on a 10km square basis.

● Present

● Extensive

Giant hogweed

33

displace native plants. Himalayan balsam can also displace native plants, spreading prolifically by seed explosively propelled from ripened pods.

3.38 The distribution of these plants at RHS reference sites is shown in Figures 31 - 33. It is particularly noteworthy that 17.8 per cent of RHS reference sites with semi-natural channel structure have one or more of these three alien plant species present.

Japanese knotweed

Figure 32 The occurrence of Japanese knotweed at RHS reference sites, on a 10km square basis.

- Present
- Extensive

Figure 33 The occurrence of Himalayan balsam at RHS reference sites, on a 10km square basis.

- Present
- Extensive

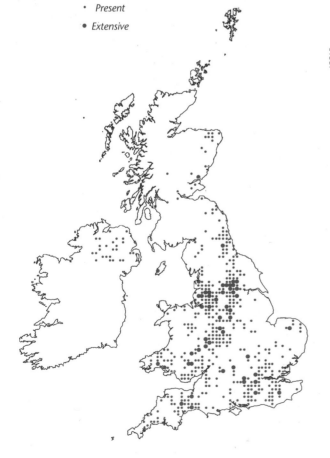

Himalayan balsam

Chapter 4 Quality assessment using four contrasting river types

• regional differences • steep streams • mountain valley rivers • chalk rivers •
• small, lowland riffle-dominated rivers •

Background

4.1   The RHS database can be used to establish the distribution of those reference sites containing any particular feature or combination of features. It can also be used to relate these features to river type, location, past management, or other relevant factors. In Chapter 3, two very simple selection rules were used to distinguish between sites located in upland and lowland areas, as required for a general overview.

4.2   This Chapter uses four, more specific river types to demonstrate how results describing physical character and habitat quality can be presented. Each river type chosen represents a small subset of the total number of RHS reference sites, having its own distinctive character (Figure 34), and a well-defined geographical distribution. For the purposes of this

Figure 34 Flow-related features in semi-natural channels of four different river types. *1996 data.*

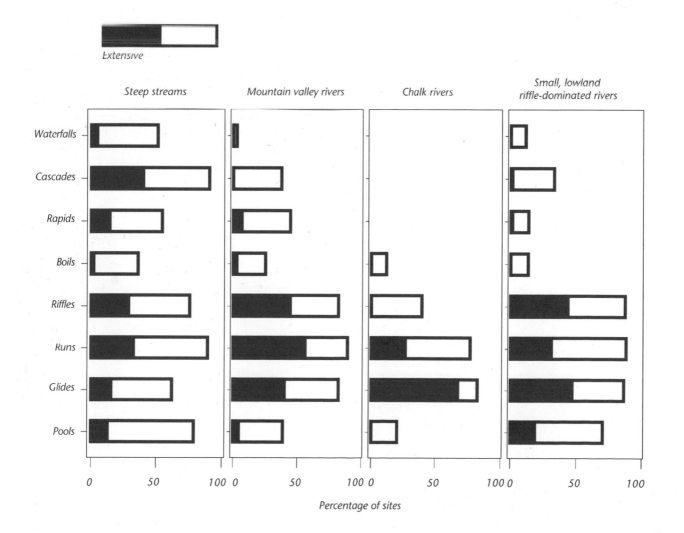

Chapter the four types selected are:

- steep streams
- mountain valley rivers
- chalk rivers
- small, lowland riffle-dominated rivers.

4.3   The selection rules that have been used to determine these four types for the purposes of this Report are highlighted in the following sections. Figures 35-38 provide a summary presentation of predominant channel features, valley form, land use, distribution of sites, HQA and HMS scores, and major impacts for each of the four types. More comprehensive lists of features associated with each of these types appear in Appendix 4.

4.4   In passing, it is important to note that the four types used are purely to illustrate how results can be presented. Together, they account for 21 per cent of RHS reference sites. Selection rules can be used to define any number of river types, but this process needs to be informed by sound professional judgment and peer review. For this reason, great care must be exercised, since conclusions from the resulting analysis of features could be subjected to detailed scrutiny, possibly at a Public Inquiry.

Steep streams

4.5   Accounting for six per cent of RHS reference sites, steep streams are found extensively in areas of hard geology, often set in a moorland or woodland landscape (Figure 35). They are characterised by a diverse variety of flow types, with features such as cascades, exposed bedrock and boulders, and liverwort and moss vegetation predominant. Headwater reaches may dry up in periods of

Waterfall more than 5m high

prolonged dry weather. In most cases, steep valley and channel gradients prevent the development of true floodplains, but the presence of adjacent bog and wet flushes add to habitat quality.

4.6   In areas subject to historical deforestation, grazing pressure by sheep and in some cases deer means that, below the present-day tree-line, very little native broadleaf woodland or native pinewood remains. In these areas, individual trees may only survive in inaccessible craggy or steep gorge sections. Afforestation with exotic conifers in the 1950s and 1960s is also a major legacy in parts of upland Scotland and Wales, exacerbating water acidification in those catchments with calcium-poor geology.

4.7   The remoteness of many of these streams contributes to a relatively low incidence of channel modification. Bank reinforcement is often used to protect roads, forestry access tracks and footpaths, since these are at risk of erosion when heavy rain or snowmelt turns these streams into raging torrents.

Rowan trees which have survived grazing

Mountain valley rivers

4.8 Accounting for three per cent of RHS reference sites, these rivers are located in predominantly hilly or mountainous settings where high energy steep upland streams reach relatively flat valley floors (Figure 36). Because they actively meander, erode and deposit, river terraces commonly occur. Characteristic channel features include runs, riffles and glides, a cobble-dominated substrate, exposed boulders, bryophytes and unvegetated side bars. Features such as bog, marsh and braided channels add to habitat quality. When water quality and flows are good, and land-use impacts are insignificant, these rivers provide excellent fishing for salmon *Salmo salar* and sea-trout *Salmo trutta*.

4.9 Located as they are in the valley floor, land-use is predominantly rough or improved pasture, particularly in Scotland, where the flat ground to either side of the channel was often used in the historical past for crofting. In these instances, artefacts of agricultural settlement are common.

4.10 Bank reinforcement is the most frequent type of channel modification. However, efforts to restrain these actively meandering rivers often results in failure, because reinforcement on an unstable base is unsustainable.

Mountain valley rivers

Braided channel

Gabion reinforcements used to restrain the active channel of a mountain valley river (above) - such reinforcements often fail, for example, on the River Swale, Yorkshire (below)

Bank collapse and a river terrace beyond - Glen Mazeran, Highland Region

Figure 35 An overview of steep streams.

Percentage of RHS reference sites

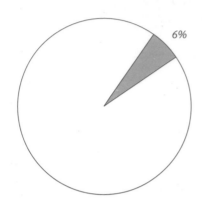

6%

Predominant features of semi-natural channels

Percentage of sites

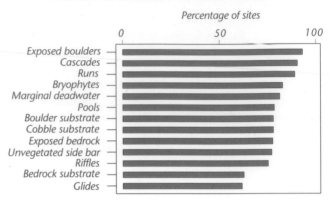

Exposed boulders
Cascades
Runs
Bryophytes
Marginal deadwater
Pools
Boulder substrate
Cobble substrate
Exposed bedrock
Unvegetated side bar
Riffles
Bedrock substrate
Glides

Valley form

Percentage of sites

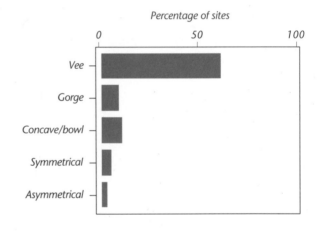

Vee
Gorge
Concave/bowl
Symmetrical
Asymmetrical

Distribution of sites on a 10km square basis

▲ Benchmark

● Semi-natural

○ Others

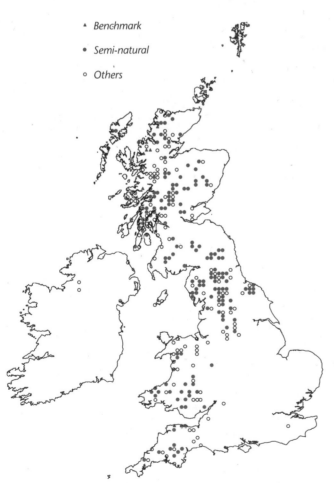

Typical steep stream - tributary of the River Traligill, Highland Region

38

HQA score

A benchmark steep stream - Torridon, Wester Ross

Number of sites vs HQA score

HMS score

Percentage of sites

0-2	
3-8	
9 20	
21-44	
45+	

Land use

Extensive

Percentage of sites

Broadleaf woodland
Conifer plantation
Orchard
Moorland/heath
Scrub
Tall herbs
Rough pasture
Improved/semi-improved grass
Tilled land
Wetland
Open water
Suburban/urban

Steep stream with reinforced bank - English Lake District

Modifications

Percentage of sites

Culverts
Weirs
Reinforced bank
Resectioned bank
Reinforced channel
Resectioned channel
Embankments
Poaching of banks

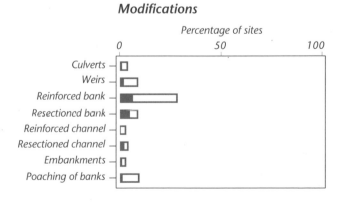

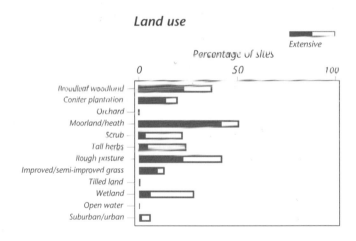

Figure 36 An overview of mountain valley rivers.

Predominant features of semi-natural channels

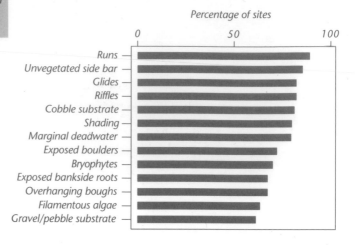

Percentage of sites

Percentage of RHS reference sites

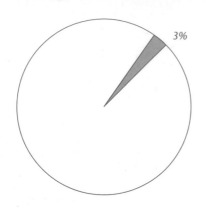

3%

Valley form

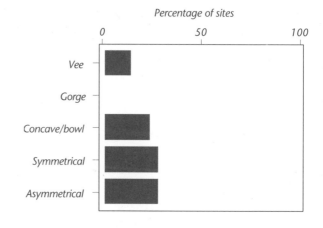

Percentage of sites

Distribution of sites on a 10km square basis

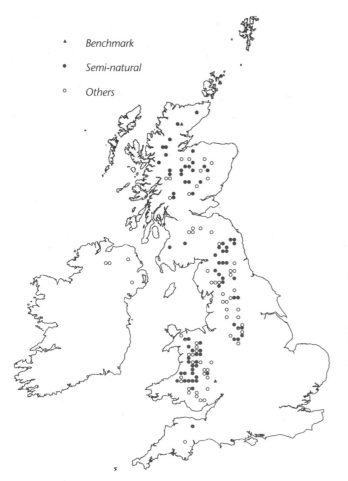

▲ Benchmark

● Semi-natural

○ Others

Typical mountain valley river - River Dee, Aberdeenshire

40

HQA score

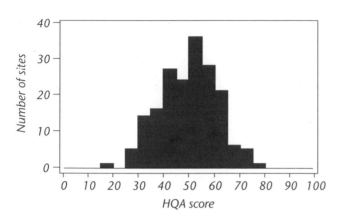

HMS score

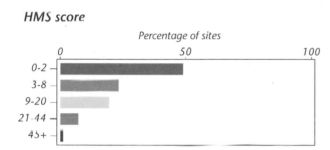

Impacted mountain valley river - River Breamish, Northumbria

A benchmark mountain valley river - River Feshie, Highland Region

Land use

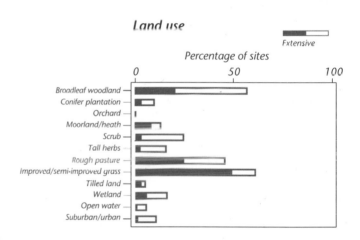

Modifications

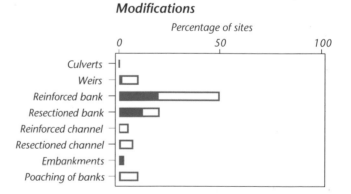

Chalk rivers

DEFINITION
• sites on Cretaceous upper chalk, not influenced by overlying glacial clays • not intermittent (winterbourne) •

4.11 Strictly speaking, these rivers are confined to areas of Cretaceous chalk that are unaffected by the hydrological influences of overlying clays and other impervious drift deposits (Figure 37). On this basis, three per cent of RHS reference sites qualify as chalk rivers. They are found exclusively in England and are fed by groundwater, producing crystal clear water and a very stable flow. In the past, they were important for water mills, water meadows and water-cress beds, and they continue to be important as game fisheries. No entire natural chalk rivers remain: only a very few, extremely short stretches still meander through remnant floodplain fen, alder carr and oak woodland.

4.12 Characteristic channel features include a clean gravel-pebble substrate, extensive runs and glides, and a typically constant depth. There are very few in-channel features, other than those provided by abundant submerged aquatic plants, notably water-crowfoot *Ranunculus* spp. and water-cress *Nasturtium* spp. The banks are low, generally less than 0.3m high, and flood events are exceedingly rare.

4.13 Traditional chalk river management includes seasonal weed-cutting, and the installation of weirs to provide deeper water for salmon and trout. Bank reinforcement using wooden boards is widespread. To provide suitable conditions for game anglers, banktop pathways are regularly mown: in addition, obstructions such as fallen or overhanging trees, and coarse woody debris are often cleared from the channel.

4.14 The effects of over-abstraction of water associated with public water supply and agricultural irrigation include channel narrowing, silting in the channel and encroachment of riparian vegetation. When combined with the effects of drought, some chalk rivers dry up well below the naturally intermittent headwaters known as winterbournes.

River Misbourne

River Till

An overabstracted chalk river-the River Misbourne, Berkshire (left). This should not to be confused with the natural seasonality of winterbournes, for example the River Till, Wiltshire (right).

4.15 A combination of resectioning and reinforcement of the channel, associated largely with agricultural land-use, produces a relatively high incidence of modifications. When carried out well, fisheries-related management of chalk rivers is one example where regular in-stream works can provide good habitat for aquatic wildlife[6]. Nevertheless, if fisheries management is stopped, the riparian habitat of chalk rivers can revert to fen and carr woodland, although such instances are extremely rare *(see page 62)*.

Small, lowland riffle-dominated rivers

> ### DEFINITION
> • site altitude between 20m and 200m • height of source less than 200m • banktop width between 2m and 15m • bedslope greater than 5m per km • not on chalk geology•

4.16 Geomorphological evidence suggests that natural alluvial rivers with a certain gradient have established riffle (and pool) sequences related to discharge, channel-width and meander frequency. For British rivers, a number of studies have found that the modal riffle-spacing is equivalent to 5-7 bankfull channel widths[33].

4.17 To establish the definition of this river type, an initial set of RHS reference sites was selected on the basis of the following attributes: an altitude and height of source of 200m or less; at least ten riffles; and a range of riffle spacing equivalent to one every four to eight bankfull-widths. The slope and width associated with sites fulfilling these predominantly semi-natural attributes were then determined and used to derive a definition of small, lowland riffle-dominated rivers. From this, all RHS reference sites conforming to the definition were identified, including those which were artificially modified. Although qualifying sites occur on various types of geology, chalk was specifically excluded as part of the rules to avoid confusion with chalk rivers *(see 4.11)*.

4.18 Accounting for nine per cent of RHS reference sites, small, lowland riffle-dominated rivers are located mainly in central and southern England (Figure 38 - pages 46 & 47). In addition to riffles, semi-natural channels of this type have predominant characteristic features associated with trees, including both bankside and underwater roots. These rivers flow through predominantly agricultural or woodland landscapes, and, given suitable water quality, often support good trout and coarse fish populations. Sites with little artificial channel modification usually retain those habitats associated with a meandering river channel, including vertical eroding cliffs, which provide ideal conditions for breeding kingfishers *Alcedo atthis*. In central and southern England, otters are now recolonising these rivers after a pollution-related absence of more than 20 years[34].

4.19 The type and occurrence of modification reflect frequent, but localised, reinforcement and resectioning associated with agriculture, urban development and transport routes. Analysis of riffle frequency in semi-natural channels compared with extensively resectioned or reinforced sites indicates that artificial modification results in longer riffle spacing and, by implication, a less diverse range of habitats (Figure 39). Because riffles frequently represent a location for biological sampling to assess water quality, the effect of modifications on the type and abundance of aquatic invertebrates in this habitat clearly needs to be examined in more detail. In the meantime, the impact of channel modifications on specific habitat features is further explored in Chapter 5.

Figure 39 Riffle spacing, expressed as bankfull widths, in semi-natural and modified channels of small, lowland riffle dominated rivers.

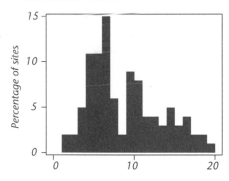

Semi-natural channels

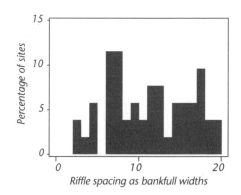

Extensively re-sectioned or reinforced channels

Riffle spacing as bankfull widths

Figure 37 An overview of chalk rivers.

Percentage of RHS reference sites

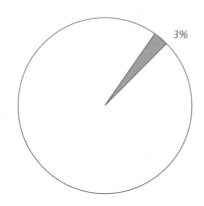

3%

Predominant features of semi-natural channels

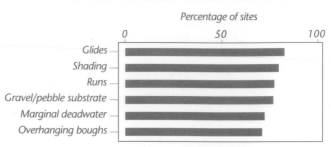

Valley form

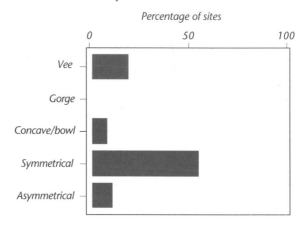

Distribution of sites on a 10km square basis

▲ Benchmark

● Semi-natural

○ Others

Typical chalk river - River Itchen, Hampshire

HQA score

A benchmark chalk river - a side channel of the River Wissey, Norfolk

HMS score

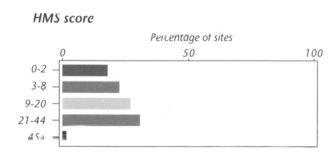

An impacted chalk river - the River Darent, Kent

Land use

Extensive

Modifications

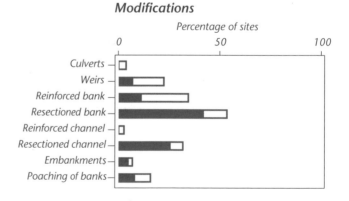

Figure 38 An overview of small, lowland riffle-dominated rivers.

DEFINITION
• site altitude between 20m and 200m • height of source less than 200m • banktop width between 2m and 15m • bedslope greater than 5m per km • not on chalk geology•

Predominant features of semi-natural channels

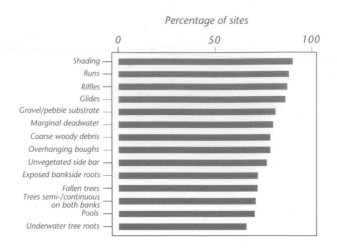

Percentage of RHS reference sites

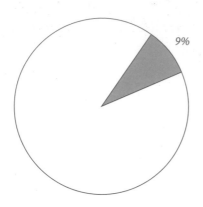

9%

Valley form

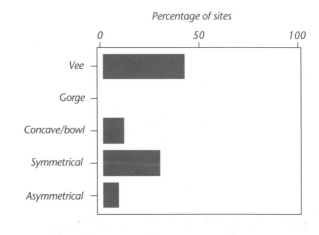

Distribution of sites on a 10km square basis

▲ Benchmark

● Semi-natural

○ Others

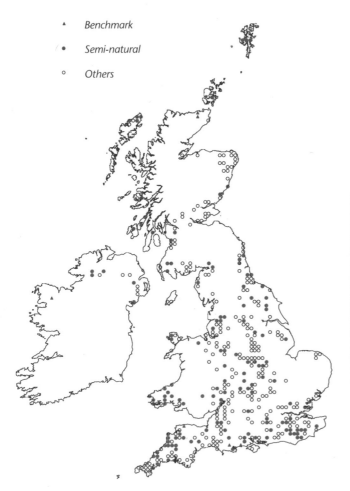

Typical small, lowland riffle-dominated river - By Brook, Wiltshire

46

HQA score

Number of sites / HQA score

A benchmark small, lowland riffle-dominated river - Highland Water, New Forest

HMS score

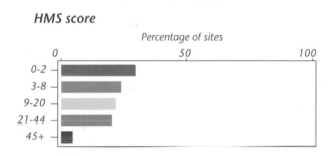

Percentage of sites

0-2	
3-8	
9-20	
21-44	
45+	

Land use

Extensive

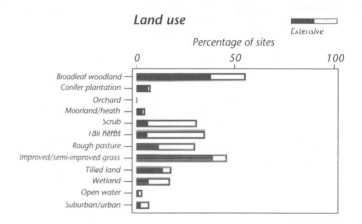

Percentage of sites

Broadleaf woodland
Conifer plantation
Orchard
Moorland/heath
Scrub
Tall herbs
Rough pasture
Improved/semi-improved grass
Tilled land
Wetland
Open water
Suburban/urban

Modifications

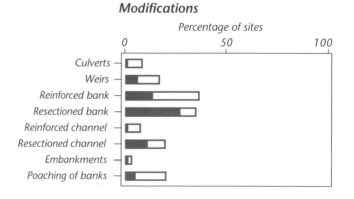

Percentage of sites

Culverts
Weirs
Reinforced bank
Resectioned bank
Reinforced channel
Resectioned channel
Embankments
Poaching of banks

Impacted small, lowland riffle-dominated river - Fairham Brook, Nottinghamshire

The range in HQA scores

4.20   The range in HQA scores for the four river types used in this Chapter is broadly the same (ca. 10 - 90), indicating a wide variation in habitat quality for each. The normal (bell-curve) distribution of scores, at least for these four river types, provides a practical basis for classifying individual RHS sites in terms of "within the top 10 per cent", which is one of the HQA - related outputs identified in Figure 6.

4.21   The importance of river corridor habitat features in determining the HQA score is evident when comparing similar sites with different land use. The two photographs below illustrate how the difference in HQA scores of two sites with semi-natural channel structure reflects the structural diversity of the river corridor.

*A steep, treeless stream with semi-natural channel structure, Highland Region (**HQA score = 32**)*

*A steep, wooded stream with semi-natural channel structure, North Exmoor (**HQA score = 54**)*

Chapter 5 Applications of River Habitat Survey

5.1 Although development of the RHS database has been a major achievement in itself, the ultimate test for the system is in the implementation of its practical applications. This Chapter provides a flavour of how it has already been used and the scope for further uses.

Catchment management plans

5.2 Catchment plans provide the necessary framework for integrated river basin management. RHS has already started to add another dimension to catchment management plans and Local Environment Agency Plans (LEAPs) by providing:

- a descriptive framework for describing the physical character, quality and modification of rivers;

- a basis for setting habitat-related targets and measuring the performance of river management;

- a link with other measures of quality so that river management can take full account of all users' requirements.

5.3 For LEAPs, it is useful to have a 'rough guide' of river character which can be used to divide the catchment into broadly similar categories based on physical attributes. The river segment map of RHS Report Number 1, with its eleven preliminary categories, currently provides such a framework[23]. The main practical use of this is to provide a broad overview of river character whereby landscape-scale comparisons within a catchment, and differences between neighbouring catchments, can be readily determined (Figure 40). It needs to be tested and refined further, but for now it serves its purpose as a guiding tool for catchment planning.

5.4 The geographical coverage of RHS reference sites provides a useful basis for the general description of river character at the regional level or

above, but extra survey work may be necessary for individual catchments, depending on the level of detail required (Figures 41 - 43). An optimum catchment-based sampling strategy, using RHS surveys every 2km (a frequency of one survey every fourth 500m), is recommended - a conclusion produced from analysing a complete survey of the River Wyre in Lancashire[35]. Entire lengths of other mainstream rivers have also been surveyed, providing a complete RHS assessment of physical character, quality and modification which has been used in conjunction with other information for catchment management purposes.

Environmental impact assessment and options appraisal

5.5 A key requirement of environmental impact assessment is determining the current value of a particular site and predicting the ecological changes likely to be caused by proposed works. This is particularly important in deciding whether a proposal is likely to have a 'significant effect' on the environment, in accordance with the EU Environmental Impact Assessment Directive (85/337/EEC). RHS can help to establish the relative importance of a site in habitat quality terms (Figure 4). Decisions on whether a full Environmental Impact Assessment needs to be carried out, plus broad policies regarding protection, mitigation and enhancement can then be related to this and other quality assessments.

5.6 Both HQA and HMS scores can be used to assist in 'before and after' appraisals of physical alterations to the river channel and adjacent land. Existing HQA scores, based on features such as trees, underwater tree roots, marginal deadwater, or riparian wetland, provide a simple numerical baseline against which losses of such features can be anticipated and real changes measured. This provides both a management tool for improving decision-making and a means of auditing decisions and the resulting consequences. It is important to note that

Structural modification - RHS can help to predict and assess the impact of such works on river habitats

RHS cannot replace other specific assessment methods, but can provide a consistent framework for deciding whether more detailed studies (such as geomorphological or botanical survey work) are required.

5.7 The RHS database allows the relationship between features and modifying factors at both site and individual spot-check level to be analysed. As more RHS sites outside the baseline reference network are surveyed (a further 5,500 RHS sites outside the reference network had been surveyed by December 1997), the platform for this analysis is expanding all the time. Analyses can be carried out on a whole range of features, comparing their occurrence in impacted and semi-natural channels of the same river type. Paragraphs 5.8 - 5.14, on pages 54 - 55 illustrate how five selected habitat features in small, lowland riffle-dominated rivers can be affected by extensive bank resectioning, bank reinforcement, and impoundment. The necessary statistical analysis required to assess the significance of impacts on these and other features is not, however, included in this Report.

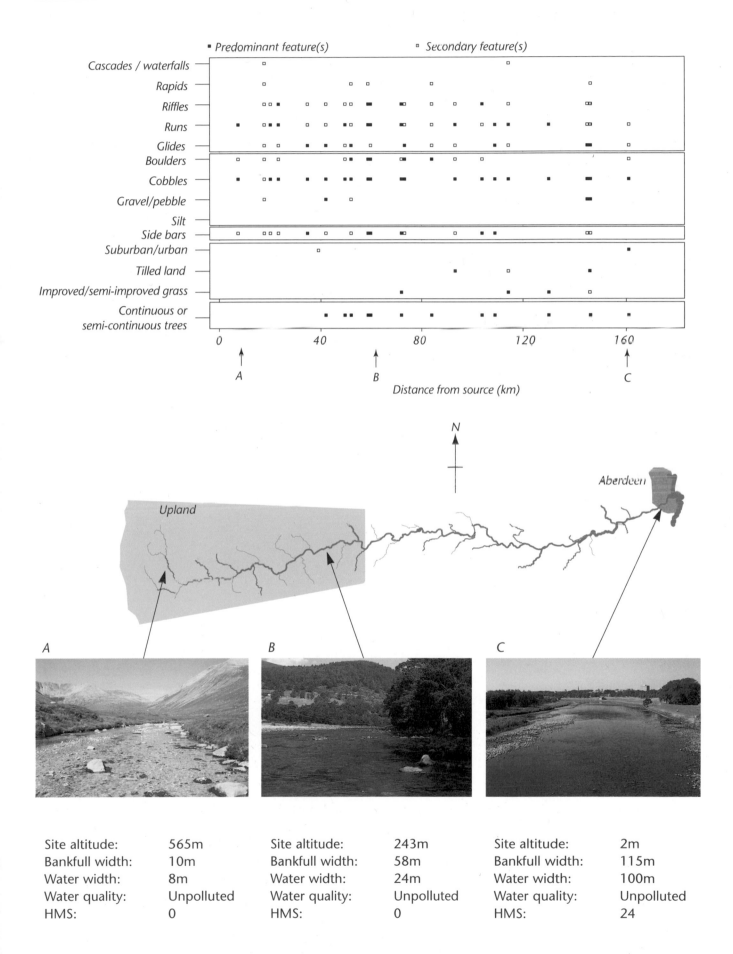

Figure 41 Downstream changes in river character along the River Dee, Scotland. *Data sources include reference and other RHS sites.*

Site altitude:	565m	
Bankfull width:	10m	
Water width:	8m	
Water quality:	Unpolluted	
HMS:	0	

Site altitude:	243m	
Bankfull width:	58m	
Water width:	24m	
Water quality:	Unpolluted	
HMS:	0	

Site altitude:	2m	
Bankfull width:	115m	
Water width:	100m	
Water quality:	Unpolluted	
HMS:	24	

Figure 42 Downstream changes in river character along the River Wye. *Data sources include reference and other RHS sites.*

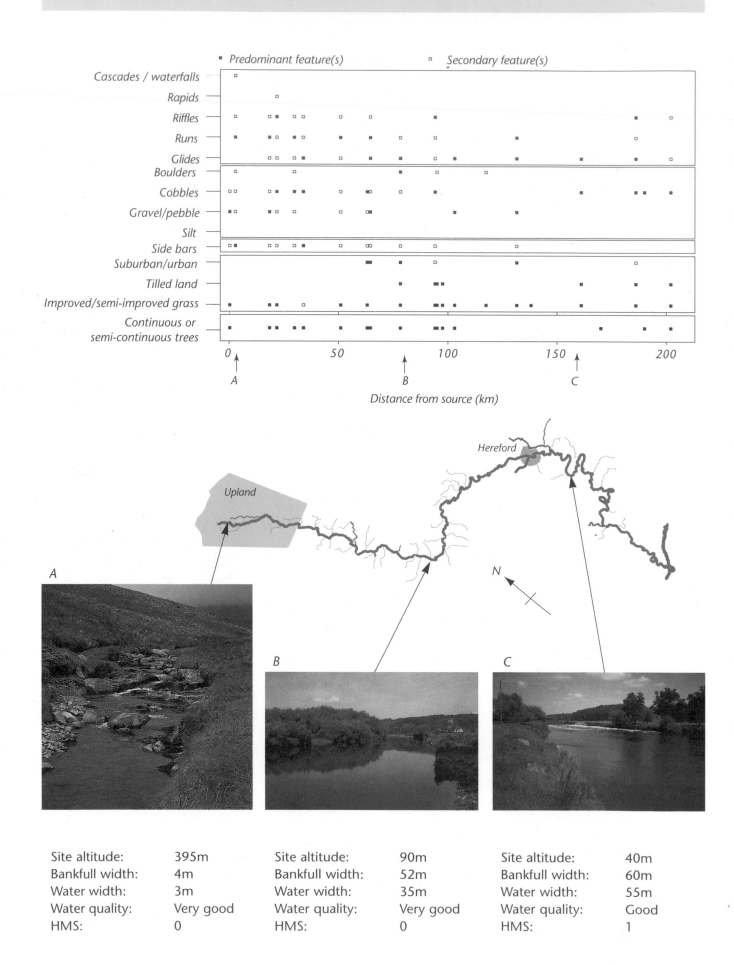

Site altitude:	395m	Site altitude:
Bankfull width:	4m	Bankfull width:
Water width:	3m	Water width:
Water quality:	Very good	Water quality:
HMS:	0	HMS:

Site altitude: 395m
Bankfull width: 4m
Water width: 3m
Water quality: Very good
HMS: 0

Site altitude: 90m
Bankfull width: 52m
Water width: 35m
Water quality: Very good
HMS: 0

Site altitude: 40m
Bankfull width: 60m
Water width: 55m
Water quality: Good
HMS: 1

Figure 43 Downstream changes in river character along the River Lagan, Northern Ireland. *Data sources include reference and other RHS sites.*

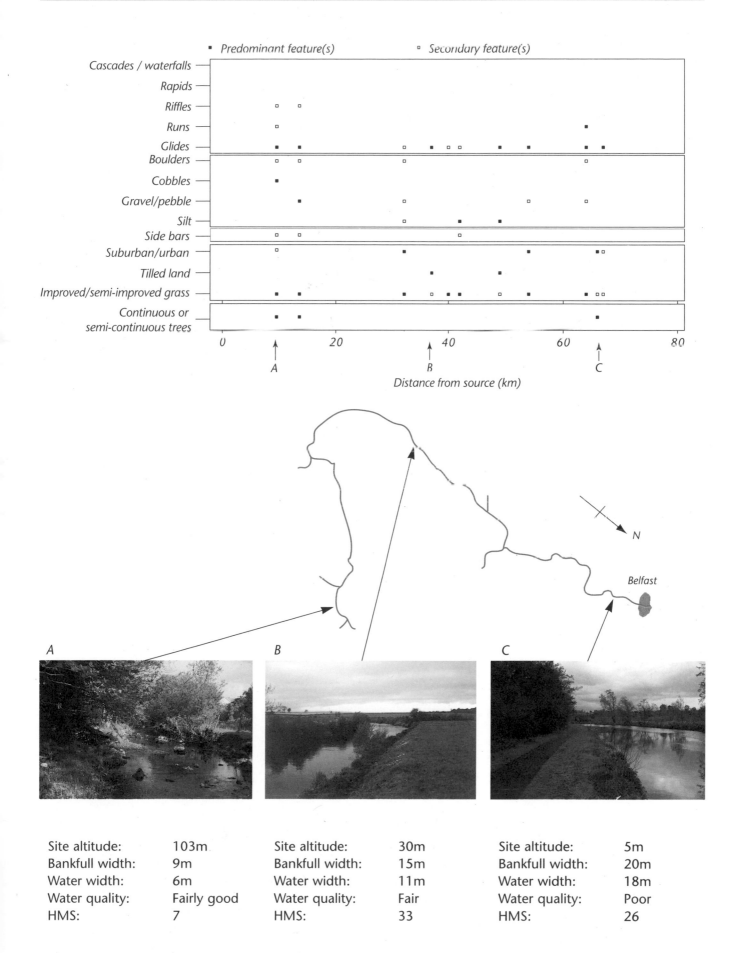

Site altitude:	103m	Site altitude:	30m	Site altitude:	5m
Bankfull width:	9m	Bankfull width:	15m	Bankfull width:	20m
Water width:	6m	Water width:	11m	Water width:	18m
Water quality:	Fairly good	Water quality:	Fair	Water quality:	Poor
HMS:	7	HMS:	33	HMS:	26

Bank resectioning

5.8   Bank resectioning is mainly associated with land drainage and flood defence works, and involves the mechanical reprofiling of the river to produce a larger, more uniform cross-section to allow faster passage of flood flows. This means dredging, often supported by regular mowing and brush clearance, to maintain a smooth channel cross-section.

5.9   Not surprisingly, there are clear adverse impacts on the diversity of both in-stream and bank habitats when resectioning is extensive. Features such as riffles, point bars, and tree cover are all affected (Figure 44). Extensively resectioned sites also have a greater preponderance of silt and less gravel/pebble channel substrate than semi-natural channels. The impact on point bars is most significant since these features occur on the inside of meander bends. Resectioning is often associated with channel straightening, which will therefore reduce the number of meanders and consequently the occurrence of point bars.

5.10   The implications for river management are clear, and confirm the need for techniques such as working from one bank to minimise environmental impact[6]. Further analysis of the RHS database should be able to quantify better which management practices are beneficial for wildlife habitats, either through minimising the loss of natural features or improving degraded reaches[6].

Bank reinforcement

5.11   Reinforcement is used to protect all or part of a bank from erosion. Various materials can be used, depending on the level of protection needed. Concrete, sheet piling, bricks, stone, rip-rap and rock-filled gabion baskets are used for 'hard' reinforcement, whilst willow spiling or reeds can be used for environmentally-friendly bank protection.

5.12   Extensive 'hard' bank reinforcement, often associated with artificially straightened channels, has a clear adverse impact on point bars and bankside trees compared with semi-natural channels (Figure 45). The effect on the diversity of channel substrate types can also be significant when the river bed is reinforced with materials such as brick or concrete.

Channel impoundment

5.13   River channels are impounded for a variety of purposes, including: to manage water levels of surrounding land; to control flooding; to abstract

water; to provide water power for driving mill wheels; to aerate water; to monitor water levels; and to diversify the in-stream habitat of featureless reaches. The impact depends both on the height of the impounding structure and the channel gradient. However, in sites with one or more weirs there is a reduction in the occurrence of riffles and point bars. The occurrence of silt as a channel substrate is noticeably greater (Figure 46).

5.14   Construction of weirs, for whatever purpose (fisheries, navigation, power generation), needs to take full account of the potential impact on in-stream

Point bar - a feature of meandering channels, often lost through straightening and resectioning work

Figure 44 The impact of extensive resectioning on selected habitat features of small, lowland riffle-dominated rivers.

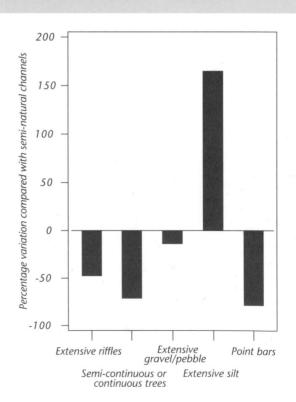

channel features and the plant and animal communities dependent on them. Indeed, the collapse or removal of redundant weirs can restore some of the flow-related habitat diversity lost as a result of the installation of these structures.

Habitat enhancement

5.15 Management to enhance the structural diversity of degraded rivers include the following techniques: gravel bars to mimic riffles; deflector groynes to diversify flow; tree-planting; channel and bank reprofiling to create more natural slopes; and fencing-off the inside of bends to allow scrub development[6].

'Hard' bank reinforcement

Concrete

Concrete and brick

Sheet piling

Gabion reinforcement and, on lower bank, rip-rap

Environmentally-friendly bank reinforcement

Wooden stakes and reeds

One year later

Deidre Murphy

Figure 45 The impact of extensive reinforcement on selected habitat features of small, lowland riffle-dominated rivers.

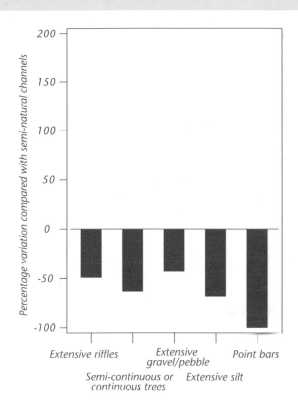

Extensive riffles

Extensive gravel/pebble

Point bars

Semi-continuous or continuous trees

Extensive silt

Figure 46 The impact of impoundment by weirs on selected habitat features of small, lowland riffle-dominated rivers.

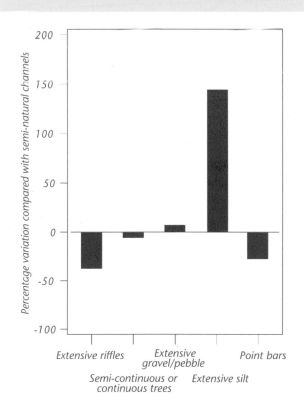

Extensive riffles

Extensive gravel/pebble

Point bars

Semi-continuous or continuous trees

Extensive silt

5.16 The RHS database can help to assess likely changes in features and habitat quality associated with enhancement and rehabilitation measures for degraded rivers. In some instances, well-intentioned enhancement works, such as riffle reinstatement or pool excavation, can be inappropriate for a particular location. Gravel imported to form 'riffles' can be left high and dry, or, in other instances, swept away by major spates, if located in the wrong place.

5.17 The risk of rehabilitation failure can be reduced by providing information on channel character and behaviour. Decisions on the re-introduction of features such as riffles can be made more confidently using the RHS database, because the pattern of their occurrence in other sites of the same river type can be determined. In this way, sustainable and effective solutions can be more readily identified.

5.18 RHS alone cannot produce the answers. In all cases, RHS information should be used with other available data to guide decisions. Geomorphological principles also need to be applied, taking full account of catchment characteristics, historical influences and those sedimentary processes which are operating at the reach level[36].

5.19 River rehabilitation on a major scale requires considerable planning. Reintroduction of meanders, opening up filled-in back channels, raising bed levels and restoring floodplain wetlands is costly. However, the rewards can be great. Geomorphological information, including RHS data, can help predict changes in habitat features, to maximise the benefit to wildlife and minimise the risks of failure. This is of great importance in the cost-benefit evaluation phase of a project. Demonstrating cost-effective environmental benefits is particularly important in persuading potential funders to participate in such high-profile schemes.

Habitat quality assessment in a broader context

5.20 Quality assessment extends beyond wildlife conservation[37]. For example, anglers, canoeists, and landscape artists will all have their own ideas about the relative importance of river-related features. In each instance, a set of selection criteria can be established to determine quality according to the particular interest group. Within the limits imposed by the level of detail of features recorded, the RHS database can be used to help identify those sites which can be considered of good quality for a particular purpose.

5.21 Features representing high quality for wildlife conservation will invariably differ, to a lesser or greater extent, from those desired by other interest groups. Anglers, for example, require sufficient gaps in tree cover to allow for unimpaired casting, whilst low overhanging boughs, extensive coarse woody debris and debris dams will impede canoeists. Walkers need good access along the bank, whilst river engineers require a uniform, smooth, channel form where efficient, unimpeded flood conveyance is critical (Box 8).

5.22 Using RHS to help establish the suitability of sites for different individual uses, or a combination of uses, could be a useful tool for revealing the extent of potential conflicts and synergies associated with river management requirements at a catchment, or regional scale.

5.23 Habitat requirements for different aspects of wildlife conservation also vary. Once again, the RHS database can help to reveal the distribution of sites which represent high quality for certain species. If habitat and food requirements are well established, selection criteria can be used to help predict the potential occurrence of a particular species, provided that water chemistry and other specific requirements

Box 8 Selected features and attributes of rivers which contribute to (✓), or detract from (X), the requirements of some different interests. *Neutral effect shown as ----.*

Feature or attribute	Wildlife conservation	Fishing	Flood defence	Canoeing
Variety of flow types	✓	✓	----	✓
Low overhanging boughs	✓	----	X	X
Extensive coarse woody debris	✓	✓ or X*	X	X
Debris dams	✓	✓ or X*	X	X
Extensive fallen trees	✓	✓ or X*	X	X
Easy bank access	X	✓	✓	✓

* NB: woody debris and fallen trees create good habitat for fish, but, by creating blockages, can be considered undesirable by some fishing interests.

River Wissey side channel - unmanaged wildlife haven

River Wissey main channel - managed for fisheries

Good kingfisher nesting habitat - River Yeo, Devon

A plant-rich, uniform channel - Old Bedford River SSSI, Cambridgeshire

are also met[38, 39]. The presence of required features at a site will not always mean occurrence of a particular species, because there are many biotic interactions and non site-specific factors which also need to be taken into account.

5.24 By imposing selection criteria based on habitat requirements for a particular species, but bearing in mind the uncertainties of other factors, this approach would be similar to identifying sites of high quality using specific combinations of features (*cf* Figure 4). In effect, permutations such as "good kingfisher nesting habitat" are almost endless.

5.25 In similar fashion, those stretches of river highly valued for geomorphological reasons have been determined by a set of qualifying criteria based largely on the presence of unusual erosion and deposition features either singly or in combination, and the presence of 'historical' fluvial landforms[40].

Protecting special sites

5.26 The statutory mechanism for protecting the best wildlife conservation sites in Great Britain is through Sites of Special Scientific Interest (SSSIs). Areas of Special Scientific Interest (ASSIs) fulfil a

similar purpose in Northern Ireland. Sites of European importance (SPAs and SACs) form part of the SSSI/ASSI series and are identified using specific criteria. The selection of river SSSIs has been based primarily on the presence of specific river plant communities, with invertebrates and other key taxa, including fish and mammals, also taken into account[41,42].

5.27 This means that a number of river reaches which have excellent physical structure lie outside the current statutory SSSI and ASSI networks. Conversely, some reaches of a river SSSI which support excellent plant or animal communities may have a relatively poor channel habitat structure.

5.28 RHS can help to identify sites with naturally good physical structure in an overall, regional or even local context *regardless* of statutory status. Those concerned with wildlife and geomorphological conservation, planners and potential developers, can therefore use RHS, together with other methods such as SERCON, to establish the relative importance of a site, or a series of sites. This means that decisions to refuse or allow development proposals in the wider countryside to go ahead can be taken on a more consistent, defensible basis including the rationale for mitigation measures, if necessary.

5.29 RHS has already been used in this way. In 1996, the Countryside Council for Wales (CCW) commissioned RHS surveys of eight upland streams in Snowdonia which developers had suggested would be hydrologically suitable for small hydropower schemes. Survey results were compared with relevant reference sites in the RHS database. By applying criteria such as the presence of specific channel features, continuous tree cover and extensive broadleaf woodland on both banks, it was concluded that because each site had high habitat quality in the context of other similar RHS reference sites, development would be inappropriate[43].

5.30 Because only two of the proposed hydropower sites were within an SSSI, the use of RHS provided a useful basis for deciding whether or not to object to planning applications affecting rivers in the wider countryside. As a general principle, developers can better understand the rationale for a particular response to a planning application because site quality is put in a wider, more objectively-based, context. Environmental impact assessment is therefore a key area for using RHS to complement or support other measurements of site quality.

Chapter 6
Conclusions and forward look

• achievements so far • the current state of river habitats • further developments • linking into other systems • beyond the UK • future challenges •

About River Habitat Survey

6.1 River Habitat Survey (RHS) provides a standard method and a powerful new tool for helping to describe and assess the physical character of rivers and modifications affecting them. The database of RHS reference sites represents a unique source of baseline information on the physical character of rivers in the UK and the Isle of Man, and is the first of its kind worldwide. Results can be analysed and presented at individual site level or collectively at catchment, regional or national level, with the user determining the necessary rules to produce the required information.

6.2 Habitat quality assessment can be made in a number of ways using RHS. For example, sites which have particular habitat value for wildlife can be identified from the database on the basis of the occurrence of rare features within a particular geographical region, or a rare combination of features for a particular river type. Comparison of habitat quality based on the HQA scoring system can **only** be carried out between sites of similar river type. Selection rules determining river type have to be meaningful and subjected to peer review to ensure consistency. Consequently, development of protocols for determining river type will be an important part of the implementation stage of RHS.

6.3 RHS has already demonstrated its practical uses in environmental impact assessment and catchment planning. The potential for developing other applications, particularly with regard to river channel behaviour and stability, is significant. By linking with other systems, RHS can help to provide a sound basis for setting and monitoring environmental targets to maintain, improve and report on river quality as a whole. This can be used to guide land and river management policies as well as helping to target action and measure performance of key river habitats as required by the UK Biodiversity Action Plan.

6.4 RHS has fulfilled its original development requirements, by producing:

- a proven standard field method, together with qualifying accreditation controls for surveyors;

- a geographically representative, baseline sample of habitat features and modifying factors associated with the 85,000 km of rivers and streams shown on 1:250,000 scale maps and classified for water quality;

- a computer database of reference sites throughout the UK and the Isle of Man, against which, using map-derived and field data, any other RHS site can be compared;

- a means for assessing and comparing the physical structure and habitat quality of sites based on naturalness, diversity, rarity, and an HQA scoring system calibrated using benchmark sites;

- proven uses for conservation and potential practical applications for other aspects of river management.

6.5 This Report marks the end of the initial development stage of RHS. Current assumptions now need to be tested so that further development of RHS applications can be realised and implemented.

About the current state of rivers and streams

6.6 From a snap-shot baseline sample of more than 5,600 RHS reference sites across the UK and Isle of Man, the following key points emerge about the current physical state of the 85,000 km of rivers and streams shown on 1:250,000 scale maps and classified for water quality:

- very few pristine lowland channels flowing through semi-natural landscapes remain;

- only 13.6 per cent of lowland sites in England and Wales, 28.0 per cent in Scotland and 10.1 per cent in Northern Ireland have an entirely unaltered channel - the rest are modified, but some only to a relatively minor extent;

- 3.7 per cent of lowland sites in England and Wales, 1.7 per cent in Scotland, and 5.0 per cent in Northern Ireland can be classified as having severely modified channels;

- land drainage, flood defence, intensive agriculture and urban development have significantly altered the channel shape and river landscape of many sites in the lowlands;

- extensive reinforcement and resectioning of river banks, and channel impoundment, can cause a significant reduction in habitat diversity;

- only 4.2 per cent of sites below 50m, with adjacent floodplain, have extensive wetlands, reflecting historical land drainage and current land-use pressures affecting many river corridors;

- despite the extent of channel modification, rivers and streams still represent important landscape features in many areas, particularly in intensively farmed and urban areas where riparian vegetation and riverside trees provide important structural diversity;

- the vulnerability of rivers to colonisation by invasive alien plant species is indicated by the widespread occurrence of giant hogweed, Japanese knotweed and Himalayan balsam.

Future development and applications of RHS

6.7   Close links between RHS and other systems, such as SERCON, have already been made, enabling a better overall assessment of rivers to be carried out. Given that the RHS reference sites are located on rivers classified for water quality, the simplest and most effective link is that with the chemical and biological assessment systems. Figure 47 illustrates this link, giving examples of the relationship between habitat modification scores and chemical water quality. Given appropriate survey data, a site can now be classified according to river plant community type[26], chemical and biological water quality[10], HQA and HMS score, fisheries status[44] and others currently under development, such as the macrophyte trophic ranking system.

Figure 47 Linking chemical water quality and habitat modification. *Two water quality classes shown as examples.*

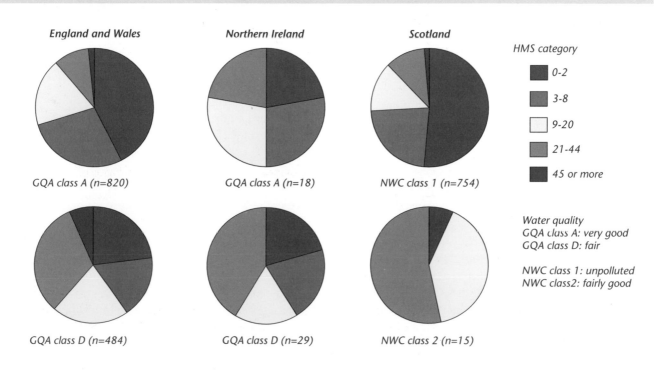

England and Wales

Northern Ireland

Scotland

HMS category
- 0-2
- 3-8
- 9-20
- 21-44
- 45 or more

GQA class A (n=820)

GQA class A (n=18)

NWC class 1 (n=754)

GQA class D (n=484)

GQA class D (n=29)

NWC class 2 (n=15)

Water quality
GQA class A: very good
GQA class D: fair

NWC class 1: unpolluted
NWC class2: fairly good

6.8 The RHS system is now operational with an initial set of applications (Box 9). The emphasis now passes to the systematic development of further planning, options appraisal and operational tasks. This Report therefore marks the beginning of the application phase.

6.9 During the development phase, RHS targeted applications focused on habitat quality assessment, with a strong link to biodiversity issues. The application phase will provide a new dimension by adding similar emphasis on channel behaviour. This will mean exploring further those geomorphological aspects of river channel stability and sensitivity, and the role of water quantity (both high and low flows), which together are major considerations for sustainable river management[33].

6.10 So far, the RHS database has provided mostly site-based outputs. There is considerable potential for using RHS data for categorising, on a catchment basis, the nature of direct and indirect impacts on river channels. It is clearly possible to look at sequences of site data within an individual catchment, or at comparative locations between catchments. This approach is needed to investigate the relationship between the 'driving' variables of gradient, flow and substrate and the influence of channel management, flow regulation, land use and other features, such as lakes and wetlands.

6.11 Linking RHS with other survey and map information through Geographical Information System (GIS) has tremendous potential. This would help to provide an assessment of river quality at the site, landscape, catchment and broader overview scales[45]. Linking into GQA measurements of river water quality, the Environment Agency's flood defence management system and the Joint Character Areas Map of England produced by English Nature and the Countryside Commission are just a few examples.

6.12 Analysis of RHS data, together with other quality assessments, could also be used to determine the effectiveness of planning designations, such as SSSIs, Areas of Outstanding Natural Beauty (AONBs) and National Parks, in conserving river landscapes[46]. RHS provides a ready-made tool to help monitor the effectiveness of waterside-focused agri-environment schemes, whilst progress on river-related actions identified in the UK Biodiversity Action Plan, particularly for chalk rivers, could be assessed by including RHS data in the National Biodiversity Network[13].

6.13 RHS can describe the habitat character of chemical and biological sampling points used for assessing water quality and it will be used to survey the freshwater sites included in the *Countryside 2000* project[46, 47]. Indeed, because habitat conditions influence the type of aquatic invertebrate communities present in rivers, RHS could provide a calibration method for assessing the impact of channel modification at biological sampling sites. RHS also has the potential to help design a habitat-

---

Box 9 Some current and future uses and users of RHS.

How RHS has already been used

- Environmental Impact Assessment *(Agency, CCW, National Parks, SNH, water companies)*
- Descriptive summary statistics and setting targets for catchment plans/LEAPs *(Agency, SEPA)*
- Monitoring and post-project appraisal *(Agency, SEPA, SNH)*
- National and Regional reporting *(Agency, SEPA, EHS)*
- 'Quality' component to complement descriptive map-based river corridor surveys *(Agency, CCW, SNH)*
- Linking with SERCON *(Agency, SEPA, SNH, EN, CCW, EHS)*
- Predicting the likely distribution of aquatic species based on their habitat requirements (for example, otter, dipper, water vole) *(Agency, SEPA, universities)*
- Linking to macrophyte trophic ranking assessment of water quality *(Agency)*

Future uses

- Input to the National Biodiversity Network *(DETR)*
- Biodiversity Action Plan target-setting and monitoring *(Agency, SEPA)*
- Targeting and monitoring waterside agri-environment schemes *(MAFF, SEPA)*
- Habitat quality calibration of sites sampled for water quality purposes *(Agency, SEPA)*
- Calibration of *Countryside 2000* freshwater sites *(DETR)*
- Linking to *Joint Character Areas* maps *(EN/CoCo)*
- Educational interactive CD-ROM *(schools, universities)*
- Calibration for remotely-sensed data *(Agency)*
- Linking into the Flood Defence Management System *(Agency)*

flow sampling protocol[48]. Calibrating aerial and remote sensing surveys of rivers using RHS field data is yet another avenue to explore.

6.14   The RHS reference sites provide a baseline for monitoring future changes in the physical character of rivers. Resurvey of a subset of the RHS reference sites could be used to help assess long-term habitat changes in different river types. Targeted monitoring could help to reveal how changes in catchment and riparian land use affect river habitat quality. For instance, the European Union's *Agenda 2000* initiative is likely to have a significant effect on habitats, because proposals for reallocating regional funding, plus reform of the Common Agricultural Policy, are likely to result in long-term land use change. In the context of climate change, alterations to habitats might result from reduced baseflows in groundwater-fed streams on the one hand, and increased flood peaks on the other, caused by the increased frequency of droughts and storms respectively.

6.15   Although RHS has been designed primarily for conservation purposes, its geomorphological context has considerable significance in its own right[48]. Analysis of overall and regional patterns, and the establishment of geomorphological benchmarks are just two examples of further development potential in this field of study.

6.16   RHS has considerable educational potential. As a result, a pilot-stage interactive CD-ROM version of the RHS database is currently being developed for specific Key Stage topic areas in the National Schools Curriculum for England and Wales. More detailed RHS data can be tailored specifically for undergraduate and post-graduate courses and for doctoral thesis studies.

6.17   By adapting and simplifying the RHS field survey method, but retaining the principles, it is hoped that interested schools or local communities will adopt their local river or stream for study. Using the RHS database, interest groups could compare the character and quality of 'their' river with similar rivers elsewhere.

6.18   The RHS field method has been developed specifically for the scale and management of rivers found in the British Isles and is not suitable for very large rivers or multi-thread channels. However, the underlying principles can be applied to larger-scale continental rivers and to channels in areas of higher, steeper relief, even if individual components such as sample length, distance between spot-checks, or vegetation-type categories, have to be adapted to suit local conditions.

6.19   The standard RHS method has already been used to generate a database and map of the physical character of rivers in Madeira, where survey work was funded by the European Union through the Laboratory of the Regional Engineer, Madeira, and undertaken in conjunction with the Institute of Freshwater Ecology. RHS surveys have also been undertaken, in the standard or modified format, for scientific purposes in Nepal[49], Slovenia, Hungary and Kenya.

RHS locations overseas

Nepal

Kenya

Madeira

A forward look

6.20 Many rivers in the UK have the potential to be altered, for better or worse, by further management intervention. Because the habitat quality of rivers matters to people, it is important that this is taken into full account when public money is spent on activities which may detract from river habitat quality. This is particularly so if this results in the removal of features or attributes which people consider important, such as trees, structural variety and access. Together with other systems, RHS can assist in this process by helping to present a range of consequences for wildlife, landscape and public amenity which could arise from anticipated changes to the physical character of rivers.

6.21 The current level of structural modification to lowland rivers and streams is likely to increase in future, primarily as a result of extra demands for new houses and improved transport links[50]. The intrinsic value of those remaining reaches with little or no channel modification will therefore increase accordingly. This underlines the need for the local and regional context to be considered when assessing whether or not a development proposal is likely to have a significant effect on the river environment.

6.22 Degraded rivers cost far more to maintain than those in better harmony with the natural functioning of running waters and their wetlands. The focus for river management in future will undoubtedly be one of cost-effective environmental improvement. Degraded rivers can best be improved by tackling water and habitat quality in a co-ordinated way. RHS information can help to establish priorities and determine which habitat features most need to be restored.

6.23 Improving the environmental quality of rivers means maximising the habitat potential for a given use or combination of uses. The extension of agri-environment incentive schemes which favour the development of riverside wildlife corridors is one of a number of mechanisms available. There is much improvement potential still to exploit. If sustainable development and biodiversity are the cornerstones for a better environment in the UK, then any future changes in river habitat quality should be measured using the results generated by the baseline RHS reference network, some of which are presented in this Report.

The Bere Stream, Dorset - showing how, in the absence of bankside management, riparian vegetation of a chalk river is reverting to carr woodland

References and further reading

References cited in the text

[1] Rackham O. (1986). *The History of the Countryside.* Dent, London.

[2] Environment Agency (1997). *The Quality of Rivers and Canals in England and Wales 1995.* Environment Agency, Bristol.

[3] Environment and Heritage Service (1997). *River Quality in Northern Ireland 1995.* Environment and Heritage Service, Belfast.

[4] Scottish Environment Protection Agency (1997). *Water Quality Survey of Scotland, 1995.* Scottish Environment Protection Agency, Stirling.

[5] Environment Agency (1998). *Understanding riverbank erosion.* Environment Agency, Bristol.

[6] RSPB, NRA & RSNC (1994). *The New Rivers and Wildlife Handbook.* RSPB, Sandy.

[7] Environment Agency (1996). *The Environment of England and Wales - a Snapshot.* Environment Agency, Bristol.

[8] Department for Culture, Media and Sport (1997). *UK day visits survey.* Signal Press, London.

[9] National Rivers Authority (1995). *National Angling Survey 1994.* NRA, Bristol.

[10] Nixon S.C., Clarke S.J., Dobbs A.J. & Everard M. (1996). *Development and testing of General Quality Assessment Schemes.* NRA R&D Report 27, HMSO, London.

[11] Commission for the European Communities (1997). Proposal for a Council Directive establishing a framework for Community action in the field of water policy. CEC COM(97)49 *Official Journal*, C184, 17 June 1997.

[12] Department of the Environment (1994). *Biodiversity: the UK Action Plan.* Command 2428, HMSO, London.

[13] Department of the Environment (1995). *Biodiversity: the UK Steering Group Report.* Two volumes. HMSO, London.

[14] Wright J.F., Moss D., Armitage P.D. & Furse M.T. (1984). A preliminary classification of running water sites in Great Britain based on macro-invertebrate species and prediction of community type using environmental data. *Freshwater Biology*, 14, 221 - 256.

[15] Milner N., Wyatt R.J. & Scott M.D. (1993). Variability in the distribution and abundance of stream salmonids, and the associated use of habitat models. *Journal of Fish Biology*, 43 (Supplement A), 103 - 109.

[16] National Rivers Authority (1992). *River Corridor Surveys. Methods and Procedures.* NRA, Bristol.

[17] Raven P.J., Fox P., Everard M., Holmes N.T.H. & Dawson F.H. (1997). River Habitat Survey: a new system for classifying rivers according to their habitat quality. In: *Freshwater Quality: Defining the Indefinable?* Eds: Boon P.J. & Howell D.L. The Stationery Office, Edinburgh. pp 215 - 234.

[18] Environment Agency (1997). 1997 River Habitat Survey. Field Methodology Guidance Manual. Environment Agency, Bristol. Unpublished.

[19] Fox P.J.A, Naura M. & Scarlett P. (1998). The derivation and testing of a standard field method, River Habitat Survey. *Aquatic Conservation, Marine and Freshwater Ecosystems*, special issue, in press.

[20] Gibbons D.W., Reid J.B. & Chapman R.A. (1993). *The New Atlas of Breeding Birds in Britain and Ireland 1988-1991.* T. & A.D. Poyser, London.

[21] National Water Council (1981). *River Quality - the 1980 survey and future outlook.* National Water Council, London.

[22] Harper D.M., Smith C., Barham P. & Howell R. (1995). The ecological basis for the management of the natural river environment. In: *The Ecological Basis for River Management.* Eds: Harper D.M. & Ferguson A.J.D. John Wiley, Chichester. pp 219 - 238.

[23] National Rivers Authority (1996). *River Habitats in England and Wales.* RHS Report No. 1, NRA, Bristol.

24 Boon P.J., Holmes N.T.H., Maitland P.S., Rowell T.A. & Davies J. (1997). A system for evaluating rivers for conservation (SERCON): development, structure and function. In: *Freshwater Quality: Defining the Indefinable?* Eds: Boon P.J. & Howell D.L. The Stationery Office, Edinburgh. pp 299 - 326.

25 Jeffers J.N.R. (1998). Characterisation of river habitat and prediction of habitat features using ordination techniques. *Aquatic Conservation: Marine and Freshwater Ecosystems*, special issue, in press.

26 Homes N.T.H., Boon P.J. & Rowell T.A. (1998). A revised classification system for British rivers based on their aquatic plant communities. *Aquatic Conservation: Marine and Freshwater Ecosystems*, special issue, in press.

27 Department of the Environment (1996). *Indicators of Sustainable Development for the United Kingdom.* HMSO, London.

28 Barton N.J. (1992). *The Lost Rivers of London* (Second edition). Historical Publications Ltd, London.

29 Everard M. (1997). Development of a British wetland strategy. *Aquatic Conservation: Marine and Freshwater Ecosystems*, 7, 223 - 238.

30 Forestry Commission (1993). *Forests and Water Guidelines.* (3rd edition). HMSO, London.

31 Forestry Commission & Environment Agency (1997). *Phytophthora disease of alder.* Environment Agency, Bristol.

32 Environment Agency (1996). *Guidance for the control of invasive plants near watercourses.* Environment Agency, Bristol.

33 Ferguson R.I. (1981). Channel form and channel changes. In: *British Rivers.* Ed: Lewin, J. George Allen & Unwin, London. pp 90-125.

34 Jefferies D.J. (1997). The changing status of the otter in the British Isles as revealed by spraint surveys. In: *Reviews of 1996.* The Vincent Wildlife Trust, pp 19 - 23.

35 Sansbury J. (1994). The applicability of River Habitat Survey for catchment management planning. Unpublished report to the National Rivers Authority, North West Region, Warrington.

36 Newson M.D. (1997). *Land, Water and Development.* (Second edition). Routledge, London.

37 Tunstall S., Fordham M., Green C. & House, M. (1997). Public perception of freshwater quality with particular reference to rivers in England and Wales. In: *Freshwater Quality: Defining the Indefinable?* Eds: Boon P.J. & Howell D.L. The Stationery Office, Edinburgh. pp 39 - 58.

38 Naura M. & Robinson M. (1998). Principles of River Habitat Survey to predict the distribution of aquatic species: an example applied to the native, white-clawed crayfish *Austropotamobius pallipes. Aquatic Conservation: Marine and Freshwater Ecosystems*, special issue, in press.

39 Buckton S.T., & Ormerod S.J. (1997). Use of a new standardised habitat survey for assessing the habitat preferences and distribution of upland river birds. *Bird Study*, 44, 327 - 337.

40 McEwen L.J., Brazier V. & Gordon J.E. (1997). Evaluating the geomorphology of freshwaters: an assessment of approaches. In: *Freshwater Quality: Defining the Indefinable?* Eds: Boon P.J. & Howell D.J. The Stationery Office, Edinburgh. pp 258 - 281.

41 Nature Conservancy Council (1989). *Guidelines for Selection of Biological SSSIs.* NCC, Peterborough.

42 Boon P.J. (1992). The role of Sites of Special Scientific Interest (SSSIs) in the conservation of British rivers. *Freshwater Forum*, 1, 95 - 108.

43 Litton G. (1997). Environmental impact of river and stream hydropower. Unpublished report to the Countryside Council for Wales, Bangor.

44 Mainstone C.P., Barnard S. & Wyatt R.J. (1994). The NRA National Fisheries Classification Scheme. A guide for users. R&D Note 206, NRA, Bristol.

45 Environment Agency (1998). *The State of the Environment of England and Wales: Fresh Waters.* The Stationery Office, London.

46 Barr C.J. (1997). *Current status and prospects for key habitats in England. Part 5. Waterside landscapes.* Department of the Environment, Transport and the Regions, Bristol.

47 National Rivers Authority (1995). *River Quality Schemes.* NRA, Bristol.

[48] Padmore C.L. (1997). Biotopes and their hydraulics: a method for defining the physical component of freshwater quality. In: *Freshwater Quality: Defining the Indefinable?* Eds: Boon P.J. & Howell D.L. The Stationery Office, Edinburgh. pp 251 - 257.

[49] Ormerod S.J., Baral H.S., Brewin P.A., Buckton S.T., Jühner I., Rothfritz H., & Suren A.M. (1997). River Habitat Survey and biodiversity in the Nepal Himalaya. In: *Freshwater Quality: Defining the Indefinable?* Eds: Boon P.J. & Howell D.L. The Stationery Office, Edinburgh. pp 241 - 250.

[50] Department of the Environment, Transport and the Regions (1997). *Household growth: where shall we live?* Command 3471. The Stationery Office, London.

Further reading

Bailey R.G., José P.V. & Sherwood, B.R. (eds) (1998). *United Kingdom Floodplains.* Westbury Publishing, Otley.

Boon P.J. & Howell D.L. (eds) (1997). *Freshwater Quality: Defining the Indefinable?* The Stationery Office, Edinburgh.

Boon P.J. & Raven P.J. (eds) (in press). The Application of Classification and Assessment Methods to River Management in the UK. Special issue of *Aquatic Conservation: Marine and Freshwater Ecosystems.*

English Nature (1997). *Wildlife and Fresh Water: an Agenda for Sustainable Management.* Peterborough.

Hansen H.O., Boon P.J., Madsen B.L. & Iversen T.M. (eds) (1998). River Restoration: The Physical Dimension. *Aquatic Conservation: Marine and Freshwater Ecosystems,* Special issue, volume 8, 1-264.

Lewin J. (1981) (ed) *British Rivers.* George Allen and Unwin, London.

National Rivers Authority (1993). *River Landscape Assessment. Methods and Procedures.* NRA, Bristol.

Purseglove J. (1989). *Taming the Flood.* Oxford University Press, Oxford.

Technical glossary

Definitions of terms used frequently in the text are included in Box 1. Some terms have equally valid definitions for other purposes, but this glossary defines how the terms are used in this Report. Photographs are only included if they are not in the main text.

Bankface The side(s) of the channel, between the water's edge during normal or low flow, and the first significant break in slope (the banktop), where water spills out during floods.

Banktop The first significant break in slope marking the point at which floodwater spills out of the channel. In instances where the break in slope is higher than the annual flood level, then banktop is taken as the latter, sometimes marked by debris entangled in tree branches.

Baseflow River-flow derived from groundwater aquifers and springs, **not** surface run-off. The proportion of baseflow to surface run-off is expressed as Baseflow Index (BFI).

Benchmark A top quality RHS site specially surveyed for calibrating habitat quality of a particular river type.

Biodiversity An abbreviated form of biological diversity — the variety of life.

Boil A flow type where water upwells to form bubbles on the surface, particularly below waterfalls and cascades.

Braided channel Multiple channel morphology in an actively-meandering cobble-dominated river, often found where a high energy mountain stream spills onto a flat valley floor.

Bryophyte A collective term for liverworts and mosses.

Carr Wet woodland, usually alder or willow, often with a sedge understorey and peaty soils.

Cascade Chute-flow occurring over boulders or bedrock outcrops.

Channel A term used collectively in the text, and for HMS scores, meaning the course of a river or stream, including the bed and banks. RHS data can, however, be split into channel (in-stream) and bank features *(see Appendix 1)*.

Classification The grouping of RHS sites with similar attributes features, HQA or HMS scores.

Coarse woody debris Tree trunks and large branches swept downstream and temporarily occupying all or part of the channel. An important habitat for invertebrates.

Culvert Artificial structure, often concrete, for carrying water underground, or under bridges.

Debris dam Coarse woody debris blocking the channel and causing water to pond back.

Embankment Artificial flood bank built for flood defence purposes, which can be flush with the channel or set back on the floodplain.

Emergent reeds Narrow-leaved monocotyledons (such as reeds, sedges, rushes) rooted below water or along the water's edge. Examples include branched bur-reed *Sparganium erectum*, bulrush *Schoenoplectus*, reedmace *Typha*, common reed *Phragmites*, reed sweet-grass *Glyceria maxima*, rushes *Juncus* spp, and sedge *Carex* spp. Extensive reed fringes may dominate some lowland watercourses.

Emergent reeds in a lowland river

Eroding earth cliff Vertical or near-vertical river bank cliff, often undercut, showing a clean earth face. Often found on the outside of meander bends, opposite a point bar. Extensive eroding cliffs indicate an actively meandering river.

Eroding earth cliff

Exposed bankside roots Large (at least forearm-sized), exposed tree roots which can form bankside cavities ideal for otter holts.

Exposed bankside roots

Extensive The occurrence of a feature or modification along at least one third of an RHS site; can be applied to the channel and individual banks.

Fallen trees Uprooted or collapsed trees *in situ*. They provide excellent cover and, when extensive, indicate little, if any, recent river management.

Fallen tree

Feature A distinctive, readily recognised physical object or form recorded during an RHS survey *(see Appendix 1).*

Floating-leaved vegetation Plants rooted in the river-bed but with floating leaves. Examples include water lilies *Nuphar* and *Nymphaea*, broad-leaved pondweed *Potamogeton natans* and unbranched bur-reed *Sparganium emersum*. Mainly found in sluggish reaches.

Floating-leaved vegetation - white water-lily

Floodplain Periodically inundated part of a river valley floor.

Free-floating vegetation Floating weeds such as duckweed *Lemna* spp.

Free-floating vegetation - duckweed and frogbit (Hydrocharis)

Gabion Reinforcement to a river bank, comprising stones in a wire basket.

Glide A fisheries term describing a river reach where water moves effortlessly in a 'smooth' fashion.

HMS (Habitat Modification Score) Modification to the **channel** expressed as a score based upon the type and extent of artificial features at an RHS site *(see Appendix 3).*

HQA (Habitat Quality Assessment) score Habitat quality of an RHS site expressed numerically as a score based upon the extent and variety of natural features recorded *(see Appendix 2).*

In-stream That part of the channel covered by water in normal flow conditions.

Liverworts and mosses Lower plants, often abundant on exposed boulders and bedrock of upland streams. Collectively known as bryophytes.

Lowland Land below 200m, including all of England south and east of a line joining Start Point in South Devon and Flamborough Head in Yorkshire.

Machair Distinctive, low-lying coastal habitat, found in parts of north-west Scotland and the Hebrides.

Macrophyte A term for aquatic plants. See Appendix 1 for those types recorded by RHS.

Mature island Permanent mid-channel feature, often with established scrub and trees, at or above flood level height.

Mature island in the foreground

Mid-channel bar A distinctive, exposed deposit in mid-channel, usually consisting of loosely packed gravels and sands. Can be unvegetated or vegetated. Characteristic of relatively high energy streams.

Mid-channel bar

Ox-bow Old cut-off channel abandoned as a meandering river changes course.

Old river channel (oxbow)

Phytophthora disease A water-borne fungal disease of alders, first recorded in England in 1993.

© Forest Research

Base of alder stem showing tarry spots characteristic of Phytophthora disease.

Poaching Trampling of river banks by livestock.

Point bar A distinctive exposed deposit on the inside of a meander bend. Can be unvegetated or vegetated. An important habitat for riverside beetles and other invertebrates.

Pool A distinct feature of deeper water. Back currents are usually present. In dry-weather conditions, there is no perceptible flow.

Rapid An area of broken standing waves, forming distinctive whitewater conditions, normally over cobble or boulder substrate. Associated with steep gradient rivers and streams.

Whitewater rapids

Reach A length of an individual river which shows broadly similar physical characteristics.

Reference sites Those RHS sites specifically surveyed to establish a representative baseline sample of rivers and streams, known as the RHS reference site network *(see 2.12)*.

Reinforced bank Whole or part of the river bank which has been artificially strengthened for bank protection purposes.

Resectioned bank Whole or part of the bankface which has been reprofiled to increase flood flow and ease access for maintenance machinery. Normally a relatively smooth, angled slope.

Revetment A reinforcing structure to protect a river bank from erosion.

Riffle Shallow, fast-flowing water with a distinctly disturbed surface, forming upstream-facing unbroken standing waves, usually over gravel substrate.

Riffle and point bar

Riparian Bankside and immediately adjacent land.

Rip-rap Large boulders placed along a bank to protect it from erosion.

River corridor Land to either side of the river channel, extending to the limits of associated floodplain wetland, or 50m distance, whichever is the greater.

River habitat Feature or combinations of features associated with rivers which provides suitable conditions for sustaining riverine flora and fauna.

River type A descriptive term for rivers of similar physical character *(see Box 4 for determining river type)*.

Run Generally fast-moving water with a rippled surface. Often associated with a rapid or riffle just upstream, or where the channel narrows and therefore speeds up the flow.

Semi-natural channel The absence of artificial modification to at least 90 per cent of the channel as recorded by RHS, **and** a resulting HMS score of 2 or less *(see Appendix 3)*.

Side bar A distinctive exposed deposit of coarse or fine material found along the base of a bank other than the inside of a meander *(see point bar)*. Can be vegetated or unvegetated. Side bars in upland streams usually comprise coarse material, whilst in sluggish lowland rivers they are silty, and often vegetated with emergent reeds in summer.

Unvegetated side bar

Vegetated side bar

Site A 500m length of stream or river surveyed by the standard RHS method *(see Appendix 1)*.

Spate Flood flow which reaches or overtops the bank.

Spot-check One of ten locations at which physical and vegetation features of the river channel are recorded during RHS, using transect widths of 1m and 10m for physical and vegetation features respectively *(see Figure 2)*.

Submerged vegetation Plants which are rooted and completely submerged. Examples include submerged yellow water-lily *Nuphar lutea*, water-starwort *Callitriche* spp, water crowfoot *Ranunculus* spp and water milfoil *Myriophyllum* spp.

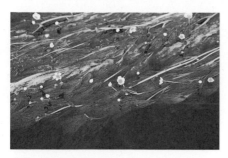
Submerged vegetation - water crowfoot

Sweep-up The process of recording features at an RHS site to complement the spot-check data *(see Appendix 1).*

Terrace An old glacial or river deposit which has been eroded to form a distinct step or terrace in the valley floor.

Terrace

Underwater tree roots Finely structured roots, which grow into the water. They provide good habitat for aquatic invertebrates such as certain damselfly nymphs, caddis larvae, and water beetles. A characteristic feature of waterside alders and willows.

Upland Land over 200m north and west of a line joining Start Point in South Devon and Flamborough Head in Yorkshire.

Vegetation structure Vegetation structure of both the bankface and banktop is an important indicator of wildlife habitat value. Along unmanaged banks at sites below the tree-line there will be a preponderance of *complex* vegetation, with plentiful shrubs and trees, although in grazed moorland sites, *simple* structure with a mixture of short woody shrubs, grasses, herbs and mosses is more likely to be predominant. *Uniform* structure (predominantly one type, such as grasses or nettles) can indicate a degraded or intensively managed bankside habitat. *(Refer to Appendix 1 to see how structure is recorded by RHS.)*

Uniform vegetation structure

Simple vegetation structure

Complex vegetation structure

Waterfall A feature of bedrock channels. Defined as free-fall flow which separates from rock and normally spans most of the wetted channel width.

Glossary of acronyms

AONB
Area of Outstanding Natural Beauty

ASSI
Area of Special Scientific Interest

CCW
Countryside Council for Wales

CoCo
Countryside Commission

DETR
Department of the Environment, Transport and the Regions

EHS
Environment and Heritage Service, Northern Ireland

EN
English Nature

EU
European Union

GIS
Geographical Information System

GQA
General Quality Assessment

HMS
Habitat Modification Score

HQA
Habitat Quality Assessment

ICOLE
International Centre for Landscape Ecology

IFE
Institute of Freshwater Ecology

LEAP
Local Environment Agency Plan

MAFF
Ministry of Agriculture, Fisheries and Food

NERC
Natural Environment Research Council

NHPA
Natural History Photographic Agency

NNR
National Nature Reserve

NRA
National Rivers Authority

NWC
National Water Council

PDF
Portable Document Format

RHS
River Habitat Survey

RSNC
Royal Society for Nature Conservation

RSPB
Royal Society for the Protection of Birds

SAC
Special Area of Conservation

SEPA
Scottish Environment Protection Agency

SERCON
System for Evaluating Rivers for Conservation

SNH
Scottish Natural Heritage

SPA
Special Protection Area

SSSI
Site of Special Scientific Interest

UK
United Kingdom

Appendix 1 RHS forms and spot-check key *Reproduced at 90% of actual size.*

1997 RIVER HABITAT SURVEY	Page 1 of 4

A   BACKGROUND MAP-BASED INFORMATION

Altitude (m)	Slope (m/km)	Flow category (1 - 10)
Solid geology code	Drift geology code	Planform category
Distance from source (km)	Significant tributary ?	Navigation ?
Height of source (m)	Water Quality Class	

B   FIELD SURVEY DETAILS

Site Number :   Mid-site Grid Reference :   River :

Date ....../....../1997   Time ....   Surveyor name ....

Accredited Surveyor ?   No ☐   Yes ☐   *If yes, state code ....*

Adverse conditions affecting survey ?   No ☐   Yes ☐   *If yes, state ....*

Bed of river visible ?   No ☐   partially ☐   entirely ☐   *(tick one box)*

Duplicate photographs : general character ?   No ☐   Yes ☐   *(tick one box)*

Site surveyed from :   left bank ☐   right bank ☐   channel ☐   *(tick as appropriate)*

SERCON survey in addition?   No ☐   Yes ☐   (tick one box)

C   PREDOMINANT VALLEY FORM   *(tick one box only)*

☐ shallow vee

☐ concave/bowl
(If U-shaped glacial valley - add "U")

☐ deep vee

☐ symmetrical floodplain

☐ gorge

☐ asymmetrical floodplain

- -

Terraced valley floor ?   No ☐   Yes ☐

D   NUMBER OF RIFFLES, POOLS AND POINT BARS   *(indicate total number)*

Riffles   Unvegetated point bars

Pools   Vegetated point bars

Spot-check 1 is at : upstream end ☐   downstream end ☐   of site *(tick one box)*

E   PHYSICAL ATTRIBUTES *(to be assessed across channel within 1m wide transect)*

[1] = one entry only	1	2	3	4	5	6	7	8	9	10	
LEFT BANK	\<td colspan="11">*Ring EC or SC if composed of sandy substrate*</td>										
Material [1] NV, BE, BO, CO, GS, EA, PE, CL, CC, SP, WP, GA, BR, RR, BW											
Bank modification(s) NK, NO, RS, RI, PC(B), BM, EM											
Bank feature(s) NV, NO, EC, SC, PB, VP, SB, VS											
CHANNEL	\<td colspan="11">*GP- ring either G or P if predominant*</td>										
Channel substrate [1] NV, BE, BO, CO, GP, SA, SI, CL, PE, AR											
Flow type [1] FF, CH, BW, UW, CF, RP, UP, SM, NP, NO											
Channel modification(s) NK, NO, CV, RS, RI, DA, FO											
Channel feature(s) NV, NO, RO, MB, VB, MI, TR											
RIGHT BANK	\<td colspan="11">*Ring EC or SC if composed of sandy substrate*</td>										
Material [1] NV, BE, BO, CO, GS, EA, PE, CL, CC, SP, WP, GA, BR, RR, BW											
Bank modification(s) NK, NO, RS, RI, PC(B), BM, EM											
Bank feature(s) NV, NO, EC, SC, PB, VP, SB, VS											

↑ Enter channel substrates not occurring in spot-checks but present in >1% whole site.

F   BANKTOP LAND USE AND VEGETATION STRUCTURE *(to be assessed over a 10m wide transect)*

Land use : choose one from BL, CP, OR, MH, SC, TH, RP, IG, TL, WL, OW, SU, RS

	1	2	3	4	5	6	7	8	9	10
LAND USE WITHIN 5m OF LEFT BANKTOP										
LEFT BANKTOP *(structure within 1m)* B/U/S/C										
LEFT BANK FACE *(structure)* B/U/S/C										
RIGHT BANK FACE *(structure)* B/U/S/C										
RIGHT BANKTOP *(structure within 1m)* B/U/S/C										
LAND USE WITHIN 5m OF RIGHT BANKTOP										

G   CHANNEL VEGETATION TYPES *(to be assessed over a 10m wide transect : use E (⩾ 33% area) or ✓ (present)*

	1	2	3	4	5	6	7	8	9	10	
NONE											
Liverworts/mosses/lichens											
Emergent broad-leaved herbs											
Emergent reeds/sedges/rushes											
Floating-leaved (rooted)											
Free-floating											
Amphibious											
Submerged broad-leaved											
Submerged linear-leaved											
Submerged fine-leaved											
Filamentous algae											

Use end "catch-all" column for types not occurring in spot checks as well as overall assessment over 500m (use E or ✓)   ↑

72

H LAND USE WITHIN 50m OF BANKTOP   *Use E (≥ 33% banklength) or ✓ (present)*

	L	R		L	R
Broadleaf/mixed woodland (BL)			Rough pasture (RP)		
Coniferous plantation (CP)			Improved/semi-improved grass (IG)		
Orchard (OR)			Tilled land (TL)		
Moorland/heath (MH)			Wetland (eg bog, marsh, fen) (WL)		
Scrub (SC)			Open water (OW)		
Tall herbs /rank vegetation (TH)			Suburban/urban development (SU)		
			Rock and scree (RS)		

I BANK PROFILES   *Use E (≥ 33% banklength) or ✓ (present)*

Natural/unmodified	L	R	Artificial/modified	L	R
Vertical/undercut			Resectioned		
Vertical + toe			Reinforced - whole bank		
Steep (>45°)			Reinforced - top only		
Gentle			Reinforced - toe only		
Composite			Artificial two-stage		
			Poached		
			Embanked		
			Set-back embankments		

J EXTENT OF TREES AND ASSOCIATED FEATURES

TREES *(tick one box per bank)*	Left	Right	ASSOCIATED FEATURES *(tick one box per feature)*	None	Present	E (>33%)
None	☐	☐	Shading of channel	☐	☐	☐
Isolated/scattered	☐	☐	Overhanging boughs	☐	☐	☐
Regularly spaced, single	☐	☐	Exposed bankside roots	☐	☐	☐
Occasional clumps	☐	☐	Underwater tree roots	☐	☐	☐
Semi-continuous	☐	☐	Fallen trees	☐	☐	☐
Continuous	☐	☐	Coarse woody debris	☐	☐	☐

K EXTENT OF CHANNEL FEATURES   *(tick one box per feature)*

	None	Present	E(>33%)		None	Present	E(>33%)
Waterfall(s)	☐	☐	☐	Marginal deadwater	☐	☐	☐
Cascade(s)	☐	☐	☐	Exposed bedrock	☐	☐	☐
Rapid(s)	☐	☐	☐	Exposed boulders	☐	☐	☐
Riffle(s)	☐	☐	☐	Unvegetated mid-channel bar(s)	☐	☐	☐
Run(s)	☐	☐	☐	Vegetated mid-channel bar(s)	☐	☐	☐
Boil(s)	☐	☐	☐	Mature island(s)	☐	☐	☐
Glide(s)	☐	☐	☐	Unvegetated side bar(s)	☐	☐	☐
Pool(s)	☐	☐	☐	Vegetated side bar(s)	☐	☐	☐
Ponded Reach(es)	☐	☐	☐	Discrete silt deposit(s)	☐	☐	☐
				Discrete sand deposit(s)	☐	☐	☐

L   CHANNEL DIMENSIONS *(to be measured at one site on a straight uniform section, preferably across a riffle)*

LEFT BANK		CHANNEL		RIGHT BANK	
Banktop height (m)		Bankfull width (m)		Banktop height (m)	
Is banktop height also bankfull height? (Y or N)		Water width (m)		Is banktop height also bankfull height? (Y or N)	
Embanked height (m)		Water depth (m)		*Embanked height (m)*	

If trashline is lower than banktop break in slope, indicate: height above water (m) =

Bed material at site is: consolidated (compact)   ☐   unconsolidated (loose)   ☐   unknown   ☐

Location of measurement is: **riffle**   ☐   run or glide   ☐   other   ☐

M   ARTIFICIAL FEATURES *(indicate total number or tick appropriate box)*

None ☐

	Major	Intermediate	Minor		Major	Intermediate	Minor
Weirs				Revetments			
Sluices				Outfalls			
Culverts				Fords			
Bridges				Deflectors			
				Other (state)			

Is water impounded by weir/dam?   No ☐   Yes, <33% of site ☐   >33% of site ☐

N   EVIDENCE OF RECENT MANAGEMENT *(tick appropriate box(es))*

None ☐   Dredging   ☐   Mowing ☐   Weed-cutting   ☐

Enhancement   ☐   Other (state)...

O   FEATURES OF SPECIAL INTEREST *(use √ or E (⩾ 33% length)*

None   ☐

Waterfalls > 5m high ☐	Artificial open water ☐	Bog ☐	Fringing reed-bank ☐
Braided/side channels ☐	Natural open water ☐	Carr ☐	Floating mat ☐
Debris dams ☐	Water meadow ☐	Marsh ☐	Other (state)......................
Leafy debris ☐	Fen ☐	Flush ☐	

P   CHOKED CHANNEL *(tick one box)*

Is 33% or more of the channel choked with vegetation?   No ☐   Yes ☐

Q   NOTABLE NUISANCE PLANT SPECIES *(Use √ or E (⩾ 33% length)*

None ☐   Giant Hogweed ☐   Himalayan Balsam ☐   Japanese Knotweed ☐   Other (state).......................

R   OVERALL CHARACTERISTICS *(Circle appropriate words, add others as necessary)*

Major impacts: landfill - tipping - litter - sewage - pollution - drought - abstraction - mill - dam - road - rail - industry - housing - mining - quarrying - overdeepening - afforestation - fisheries management - silting

Land Management: set-aside - buffer strip - headland - abandoned land - parkland - MoD

Animals: otter - mink - water vole - kingfisher - dipper - grey wagtail - sand martin - heron - dragonflies/damselflies

Other significant observations:

S   ALDERS *(tick appropriate box(es))*

Alders? None ☐   Present ☐   Extensive ☐   Diseased Alders? None ☐   Present ☐   Extensive ☐

PHYSICAL ATTRIBUTES (SECTION E)

BANKS		CHANNEL	
Predominant bank material NV = not visible BE = bedrock BO = boulder CO = cobble GS = gravel/sand EA = earth (crumbly) EA = earth CL = sticky clay CC = concrete SP = sheet piling WP = wood piling GA = gabion BR = brick/laid stone RR = rip-rap BW = builders' waste	**Bank modifications** NK = not known NO = none RS = resectioned RI = reinforced PC = poached PC(B) = poached (bare) BM = berm EM = embanked **Bank features** NV = not visible (eg far bank) NO = none EC = eroding earth cliff SC = stable earth cliff PB = unvegetated point bar VP = vegetated point bar SB = unvegetated side bar VS = vegetated side bar	**Predominant substrate** NV = not visible BE = bedrock BO = boulder CO = cobble GP = gravel/pebble (ring G or P if predominant) SA = sand SI = silt/mud CL = clay PE = peat AR = artificial **Predominant flow** *(see below)* FF = freefall CH = chute BW = broken standing waves (white-water) UW = unbroken standing wave CF = chaotic flow RP = rippled UP = upwelling SM = smooth NP = no perceptible flow NO = No flow (dry)	**Channel modifications** NK = not known NO = none CV = culverted RS = resectioned RI = reinforced DA = dam/weir FO = ford (man-made) **Channel features** NV = not visible NO = none RO = exposed bedrock/boulders MB = unvegetated mid channel bar MB = unvegetated mid-channel bar VB = vegetated mid-channel bar VB = vegetated mid channel bar MI = mature island TR = urban debris (trash)

FLOW TYPES — ASSOCIATED CHANNEL FEATURES

FLOW TYPES	ASSOCIATED CHANNEL FEATURES
FF: Free fall	clearly separates from back-wall of vertical feature ~ associated with *waterfalls*.
CH: Chute	low curving fall in contact with substrate.
BW: Broken standing waves	white-water tumbling wave must be present ~ associated with *rapids*.
UW: Unbroken standing waves	upstream facing wavelets which are not broken ~ associated with *riffles*
CF: Chaotic flow	a mixture of 3 or more 'rough' flow types on no organised pattern.
RP: Rippled	no waves, but general flow direction is downstream with disturbed rippled surface ~ associated with *runs*.
UP: Upwelling	heaving water as upwellings break the surface ~ associated with *boils*.
SM: Smooth	preceptible downstream movement is smooth (no eddies) ~ associated with *glides*.
NP: No perceptible flow	no net downstream flow ~ associated with *pools, ponded reaches and marginal deadwater*.
NO: No flow	dry.

Scale

```
        ┌─ Coarse sand
        │       ┌─ Gravel
        │       │                          Pebble                    Cobble (to size of A4 page)
        │       │                                         │
   SA   ┤       │                GP                       │                    CO
```

LAND USE WITHIN 5m OF BANKTOP (SECTION F)

BL =	Broadleaf/mixed woodland	SC = Scrub	TL = Tilled land
CP =	Coniferous/plantation	TH = Tall herbs	WL = Wetland
OR =	Orchard	RP = Rough pasture	OW = Open water
MH =	Moorland/heath	IG = Improved grass	SU = Suburban/urban
			RS = Rock & scree

BANKTOP AND BANKFACE VEGETATION STRUCTURE To be assessed within a 10m wide transect (SECTION F)

bare	B	bare earth/rock etc.	vegetation types
uniform	U	predominantly one type (no scrub or trees)	bryophytes
			short herbs/ creeping grasses
simple	S	two or three vegetation types	tall herbs/ grasses
			scrub/brambles etc.
complex	C	four or more types	saplings and trees

Channel dimensions guidance (Section L)

- Select location on uniform section.
- If riffle is present, measure there.
  If not, measure at straightest and shallowest point.

- Banktop = first major break in slope above which cultivation or development is possible.
- Bankfull = point where river first spills onto flood plain.

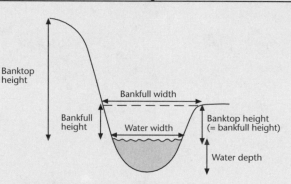

WORKING ALONE: CHECKLIST

- PREPARATION
- IMPLEMENT REPORTING-IN PROCEDURE
- WEAR PROTECTIVE CLOTHING
- DO NOT RUSH

- NEVER ENTER CONFINED SPACES
- OBSERVE HYGIENE RULES
- WATCH FOR CHANGING CONDITIONS

WEIL'S DISEASE

INSTRUCTION TO CARD HOLDERS

1. As infection may enter through breaks in the skin ensure that any cut, scratch or abrasion is thoroughly cleansed and covered with a waterproof plaster.
2. Avoid rubbing your eyes, nose and mouth during work.
3. Clean protective clothing, footwear and equipment etc., after use.
5. Report all accidents and/or injuries however slight.
6. Keep your card with you at all times.

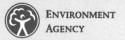 **ENVIRONMENT AGENCY**   **EMERGENCY HOTLINE 0800 80 70 60**

24 hour free emergency telephone line for reporting all environmental incidents relating to air, land and water.

Appendix 2
Habitat Quality Assessment (HQA) scoring system: version 1.2

The HQA score for a site is the total of all the component scores in the categories listed below.

FLOW TYPES

Each predominant flow-type recorded scores **1**; if it occurs at 2 - 3 spot-checks, it scores **2**; if it occurs at 4 or more spot-checks, it scores **3**. If only one type occurs·at **all 10 spot-checks**, the score will be **3**. Dry channel scores **0**.

If recorded in the sweep-up, **score 1 for each of the following channel features provided that an equivalent flow-type has not been recorded in any spot-check**: waterfall(s), if *free fall* flow absent; cascade(s), if *chute* flow absent; rapid(s), if *broken standing wave* absent; riffle(s), if *unbroken standing wave* absent; run(s), if *rippled* flow absent; boil(s), if *upwelling* absent; glide(s), if *smooth* flow absent; pool(s), if *no perceptible flow* absent. Score **1** for marginal deadwater recorded as present **or** extensive in the sweep-up.

CHANNEL SUBSTRATES

Each predominant natural substrate type (ie bedrock, boulder, cobble, gravel/pebble, sand, silt, clay, peat) recorded scores **1**; if it occurs at 2 - 3 spot-checks it scores **2**; if it occurs at 4 or more spot-checks, it scores **3**.

If only one predominant type is recorded at all 10 spot-checks, the score will be **3**.

Extra substrate(s) recorded (on the 1997 form) do **not** count.

"Not visible" does not score, unless recorded at 6 or more spot-checks, when it scores **1**.

CHANNEL FEATURES

Each 'natural' channel feature (ie exposed bedrock/boulders, unvegetated mid-channel bar, vegetated mid-channel bar, mature island) recorded scores **1**; if it occurs at 2-3 spot-checks, it scores **2**; if it occurs at 4 or more spot-checks, it scores **3**. *[NB: more than one feature can occur at a single spot-check.]*

If any of these features are **not** recorded in the spot-checks, but occur as present or extensive in the sweep-up, then they score **1** each.

BANK FEATURES

Each bank is scored **separately**.

Each natural feature (ie eroding earth cliff, stable earth cliff, unvegetated point bar, vegetated point bar, unvegetated side-bar, vegetated side-bar) recorded scores **1**; if it occurs at 2 - 3 spot checks, it scores **2**; if it occurs at 4 or more spot-checks, it scores **3**. *[NB: more than one feature can be recorded at a single spot-check.]*

If any of unvegetated point bar, vegetated point bar, unvegetated side bar or vegetated side bar are **not** recorded in the spot-checks, but appear in the sweep-up, then they will score **1** each. *[NB: vertical/undercut cliff profile recorded in the sweep-up does not equate to eroding or stable earth cliff.]*

BANK VEGETATION STRUCTURE

Only simple and complex vegetation structure score. Both score equally.

Each bank is scored **separately**.

Bankface and banktop are scored **separately**.

Bankface

If simple **or** complex is recorded at one spot-check it scores **1**; if simple and/or complex recorded at 2 - 3 spot-checks, score **2**; if simple and/or complex occur at 4 or more spot-checks, the score will be **3**.

Banktop

If simple **or** complex is recorded at one spot-check it scores **1**; if simple and/or complex recorded at 2 - 3 spot-checks, score **2**; if simple and/or complex occur at 4 or more spot-checks, the score will be **3**.

(continued)

POINT BARS

Add together the total number of unvegetated and vegetated point bars *(front page of form)*.

Score **1** if the total is 3 - 8; score **2** for 9 or more.

IN-STREAM CHANNEL VEGETATION

In-stream channel vegetation types are grouped into six categories for scoring purposes: (i) liverworts and mosses; (ii) emergent broad-leaved herbs; (iii) emergent reeds/rushes/sedges; (iv) floating-leaved, free-floating and amphibious; (v) submerged broad-leaved; and (vi) submerged linear and fine-leaved.

Score **1** for each category recorded within the site, and **2** for those categories recorded either as present or extensive at 4 or more spot-checks.

Filamentous algae do **not** score.

LAND-USE WITHIN 50m

Each bank is scored **separately**.

Only the sweep-up information is used.

Only broadleaf woodland (or native pinewood), moorland/heath, and wetland score.

Broadleaf woodland, moorland/heath and wetland each score **1** if present, and score **2** if extensive.

If broadleaf woodland (or native pinewood) or wetland, alone or together are the **only** land-use categories recorded, then score **7** for that bank. For naturally treeless sites, moorland/heath or equivalent qualifies.

TREES AND ASSOCIATED FEATURES

Trees

Each bank is scored **separately**.

Score **1** if trees are isolated/scattered; score **2** if regularly-spaced or occasional clumps; score **3** if semi-continuous or continuous.

Associated features

Overhanging boughs, exposed bankside roots, underwater tree roots, coarse woody debris and fallen trees each score **1** if present.

Extensive exposed bankside roots and underwater tree roots each score **2**.

Extensive coarse woody debris score 3.

Extensive fallen trees score **5**.

SPECIAL FEATURES

Score **5** if **any** of the following have been recorded: waterfall more than 5m high, braided or side channel, debris dams, natural open water, fen, carr, flush, bog. [*Score 5 regardless of number of special features present.*]

Footnote: HQA scores should only be used when comparing sites of similar river type or character. For instance, sites in naturally treeless exposed or mountain areas should not be compared with those in lowland wooded valleys.

Appendix 3 Habitat Modification Score (HMS) rules: version 1.1

The HMS score for a site is the total of all the component scores in the categories listed below

A. Modifications at spot-checks
(abbreviations in brackets)

	Score per spot-check
Reinforcement to banks (RI)	2
Reinforcement to bed (AR)	2
Resectioned bank or bed (RS)	1
Two-stage bank modification (BM)	1
Embankment (EM)	1
Culvert (CV)	8
Dam, weir, ford (DA, FO)	2
Bank poached by livestock (PC)	0, if less than 3 spot-checks
	1, if 3-5 spot-checks
	2, if 6 or more spot-checks

B. Modification present but not recorded at spot-checks

	One bank (or channel)	Both banks
Artificial bed material	1	-
Reinforced whole bank	2	3
Reinforced top or bottom of bank	1	2
Resectioned bank	1	2
Embankment	1	1
Set-back embankment	1	1
Two-stage channel	1	3
Weed-cutting	1	-
Bank-mowing	1	1
Culvert	8 for each	
Dam, weir, ford	2 for each	

C. Scores for features in site as a whole

	One	Two or more	Site
Footbridge	0	0	
Roadbridge	1	2	
Enhancements, such as groynes	1	2	
Site partly affected by flow control			1
Site extensively* affected by flow control			2
Partly realigned channel**			5
Extensively* or wholly realigned channel**			10

* Extensive means at least a third of channel length.
** information from map

Appendix 4 Percentage occurrence of features at RHS reference sites representing four different river types *Data refer to semi-natural channels*

Details for individual river types given on pages 81-84

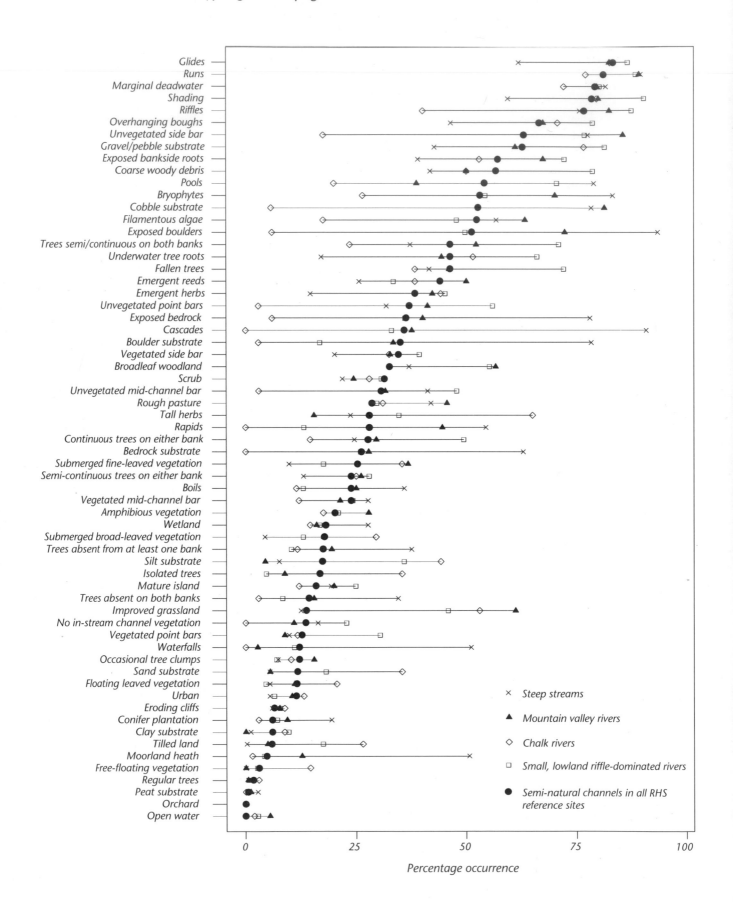

Appendix 4

The occurrence of features in steep streams

	Percentage occurrence	
	Sites with semi-natural channels	Other sites
Exposed boulders	93.4	89.5
Cascades	90.7	81.0
Runs	89.4	88.8
Bryophytes	83.1	73.7
Marginal deadwater	81.5	88.8
Pools	78.7	77.5
Boulder substrate	78.1	66.0
Cobble substrate	78.1	74.5
Exposed bedrock	77.9	62.1
Unvegetated side bar	77.3	78.4
Riffles	75.5	80.0
Bedrock substrate	62.8	50.3
Glides	61.9	69.1
Shading	59.4	78.9
Filamentous algae	56.8	46.1
Rapids	54.4	49.3
Waterfalls	51.0	43.9
Moorland/heath	50.5	25.7
Overhanging boughs	46.4	68.6
Gravel/pebble substrate	42.6	60.1
Rough pasture	41.8	40.8
Coarse woody debris	41.7	60.1
Fallen trees	41.4	55.3
Unvegetated mid-channel bar	41.1	38.6
Exposed bankside roots	38.9	54.9
No bankside trees	37.4	14.7
Trees semi/continuous on both banks	37.2	56.2
Broadleaf woodland	36.9	58.2
Boils	35.8	29.0
Trees absent on both banks	34.4	11.1
Unvegetated point bars	31.7	30.9
Vegetated mid-channel bar	27.6	20.4
Wetland	27.6	18.1
Emergent reeds	25.7	24.3
Continuous trees on either bank	24.6	33.0
Tall herbs	23.7	19.6
Scrub	21.9	33.0
Amphibious vegetation	20.2	25.7
Vegetated side bar	20.1	21.1
Conifer plantation	19.4	18.6
Mature island	19.3	18.4
Underwater tree roots	17.2	35.1
Isolated trees	16.9	14.4
No channel vegetation	16.4	17.0
Emergent herbs	14.8	31.6
Semi-continuous trees	13.1	26.5
Improved grassland	12.6	34.9
Submerged fine-leaved vegetation	9.8	7.9
Vegetated point bars	9.8	15.8
Silt substrate	7.7	14.4
Occasional tree clumps	7.4	11.4
Eroding cliffs	6.0	3.9
Floating-leaved vegetation	5.5	4.6
Urban	5.5	37.5
Sand substrate	5.5	3.3
Submerged broad-leaved vegetation	4.4	5.9
Peat substrate	2.7	0.0
Clay substrate	1.1	1.3
Regular trees	0.5	0.0
Tilled land	0.3	4.9
Free floating vegetation	0.0	1.3
Orchard	0.0	0.6
Open water	0.0	1.4

Appendix 4

The occurrence of features in mountain valley rivers

	Percentage occurrence	
	Sites with semi-natural channels	Other sites
Runs	89.0	88.2
Unvegetated side bar	85.4	71.3
Riffles	82.2	88.2
Glides	82.2	86.2
Cobble substrate	81.1	72.3
Shading	79.8	81.9
Marginal deadwater	79.5	77.6
Exposed boulders	72.2	57.4
Bryophytes	70.0	61.7
Overhanging boughs	67.4	72.3
Exposed bankside roots	67.4	72.3
Filamentous algae	63.3	56.4
Improved grassland	61.1	66.0
Gravel/pebble substrate	61.1	60.6
Broadleaf woodland	56.7	41.5
Trees semi/continuous on both banks	52.2	51.1
Emergent reeds	50.0	43.6
Coarse woody debris	50.0	46.8
Fallen trees	46.1	31.9
Rough pasture	45.6	38.8
Rapids	44.4	31.9
Underwater tree roots	44.3	51.1
Emergent herbs	42.2	42.6
Unvegetated point bars	41.1	41.5
Exposed bedrock	40.0	21.3
Pools	38.6	44.1
Cascades	37.5	21.3
Submerged fine-leaved vegetation	36.7	27.7
Boulder substrate	33.3	33.0
Vegetated side bar	32.6	39.4
Unvegetated mid-channel bar	31.5	30.9
Continuous trees on either bank	29.4	22.3
Amphibious vegetation	27.8	13.8
Bedrock substrate	27.8	17.0
Semi-continuous trees	26.1	34.6
Boils	25.0	28.9
Scrub	24.4	21.3
Vegetated mid-channel bar	21.3	20.4
Mature island	20.0	17.0
Trees absent from one or both banks	19.4	11.7
Submerged broad-leaved vegetation	17.8	13.8
Wetland	16.1	6.4
Occasional tree clumps	15.6	14.9
Tall herbs	15.6	23.5
Trees absent on both banks	15.6	8.5
Moorland/heath	12.8	1.1
Floating-leaved vegetation	11.1	5.3
No in-stream channel vegetation	11.0	18.4
Urban	10.6	39.4
Conifer plantation	9.4	8.0
Isolated trees	8.9	12.2
Vegetated point bars	8.9	16.0
Eroding cliffs	7.8	7.4
Sand substrate	5.6	4.3
Open water	5.5	2.6
Tilled land	5.0	2.7
Silt substrate	4.4	10.6
Waterfalls	2.7	3.9
Peat substrate	1.1	0.0
Regular trees	0.6	4.3
Free floating vegetation	0.0	1.1
Orchard	0.0	1.3
Clay substrate	0.0	0.0

Appendix 4

The occurrence of features in chalk rivers

	Percentage occurrence	
	Sites with semi-natural channels	Other sites
Glides	82.4	79.4
Shading	79.4	83.2
Runs	76.9	68.1
Gravel/pebble substrate	76.5	79.4
Marginal deadwater	72.0	58.9
Overhanging boughs	70.6	62.3
Tall herbs	65.0	37.0
Improved grassland	52.9	64.2
Exposed bankside roots	52.9	41.9
Underwater tree roots	51.5	43.2
Coarse woody debris	50.0	35.7
Emergent herbs	44.1	56.5
Silt substrate	44.1	55.5
Riffles	40.0	47.2
Emergent reeds	38.2	53.9
Fallen trees	38.2	22.7
Submerged fine-leaved vegetation	35.3	45.5
Isolated trees	35.3	26.2
Sand substrate	35.3	17.4
Vegetated side bar	32.4	23.2
Broadleaf woodland	32.4	38.4
Rough pasture	30.9	21.9
Submerged broad leaved vegetation	29.4	37.0
Scrub	27.9	31.3
Bryophytes	26.5	17.5
Tilled land	26.5	23.5
Semi-continuous trees	25.0	21.4
Trees semi/continuous on both banks	23.5	16.2
Floating-leaved vegetation	20.6	13.0
Pools	20.0	26.4
Unvegetated side bar	17.6	12.9
Amphibious vegetation	17.6	27.9
Filamentous algae	17.6	34.4
Free-floating vegetation	14.7	9.1
Continuous trees on either bank	14.7	7.4
Wetland	14.7	14.2
Urban	13.2	43.9
Vegetated mid-channel bar	12.1	7.1
Mature island	12.1	9.0
No bankside trees on one bank	11.8	12.6
Vegetated point bars	11.8	8.4
Boils	11.5	19.1
Occasional tree clumps	10.3	27.2
Eroding cliffs	8.8	0.0
Clay substrate	8.8	9.0
Exposed bedrock	6.1	1.9
Exposed boulders	6.1	3.2
Cobble substrate	5.9	5.2
Unvegetated mid-channel bar	3.0	7.7
Regular trees	2.9	5.2
Conifer plantation	2.9	1.0
Trees absent on both banks	2.9	7.1
Boulder substrate	2.9	0.6
Unvegetated point bars	2.9	6.5
Open water	1.9	10.5
Moorland/heath	1.5	0.0
Waterfalls	0.0	4.3
Cascades	0.0	7.8
Rapids	0.0	3.9
No in-stream channel vegetation	0.0	7.4
Orchard	0.0	0.0
Bedrock substrate	0.0	0.0
Peat substrate	0.0	0.0

Appendix 4

The occurrence of features in small, lowland riffle-dominated rivers

Percentage occurrence

	Sites with semi-natural channels	Other sites
Shading	90.1	92.0
Runs	88.2	84.2
Riffles	87.3	84.0
Glides	86.4	87.9
Gravel/pebble substrate	81.2	84.4
Marginal deadwater	80.0	67.7
Overhanging boughs	78.4	74.9
Coarse woody debris	78.4	68.8
Unvegetated side bar	76.6	58.0
Exposed bankside roots	72.1	60.8
Fallen trees	71.9	52.2
Trees semi/continuous on both banks	70.8	51.4
Pools	70.4	65.1
Underwater tree roots	66.0	53.9
Unvegetated point bars	55.9	31.3
Broadleaf woodland	55.2	45.3
Bryophytes	54.2	47.3
Cobble substrate	52.6	41.8
Exposed boulders	49.7	37.0
Continuous trees on either bank	49.3	21.7
Unvegetated mid-channel bar	47.7	30.0
Filamentous algae	47.7	50.1
Improved grassland	45.8	59.8
Emergent herbs	45.1	54.8
Vegetated side bar	39.2	33.6
Exposed bedrock	35.9	21.6
Silt substrate	35.7	50.8
Tall herbs	34.5	37.3
Emergent reeds	33.3	42.5
Cascades	32.9	26.2
Scrub	30.5	33.5
Vegetated point bars	30.3	19.0
Rough pasture	29.5	27.0
Semi-continuous trees on either bank	27.9	37.9
Bedrock substrate	26.0	11.7
Mature island	24.8	8.0
Vegetated mid-channel bar	24.2	17.3
No in-stream channel vegetation	22.7	24.6
Amphibious vegetation	20.9	32.1
Sand substrate	18.2	24.6
Submerged fine-leaved vegetation	17.6	15.9
Tilled land	17.5	26.9
Wetland	16.9	10.0
Boulder substrate	16.9	15.8
Rapids	13.2	11.0
Boils	13.1	11.1
Submerged broad-leaved vegetation	13.1	9.6
Waterfalls	11.0	7.5
No bankside trees on one bank	10.4	8.2
Clay substrate	9.7	12.3
Trees absent on both banks	8.4	5.5
Eroding cliffs	7.8	1.6
Conifer plantation	7.1	6.3
Occasional tree clumps	7.0	17.0
Urban	6.5	32.8
Isolated trees	4.7	14.5
Floating-leaved vegetation	4.6	5.8
Moorland/heath	4.2	0.5
Open water	2.7	3.0
Free-floating vegetation	2.6	5.2
Regular trees	0.7	0.7
Peat substrate	0.6	0.0
Orchard	0.0	1.4

The physical character of rivers and streams in the UK and Isle of Man

SUMMARY FACT-SHEET: MAY 1998

ABOUT THIS FACT-SHEET

This summary fact-sheet contains selected information derived from a major baseline survey of rivers and streams throughout the UK and the Isle of Man carried out during 1994–1997. Data were collected using the River Habitat Survey (RHS), a new method for assessing the physical character and quality of river habitats and the modifications affecting them. The development of this method and the main findings of the survey are described in *"River Habitat Quality: the physical character of rivers and streams in the UK and Isle of Man"*, published in May 1998 by the Environment Agency, in collaboration with the Scottish Environment Protection Agency (SEPA) and the Environment and Heritage Service, Northern Ireland.

Information is based on field observations made during a baseline survey of RHS reference sites which forms a geographically representative sample of the 85,000km of rivers and streams classified for water quality purposes. Sample sites were randomly selected within Ordnance Survey 10km grid squares, and more than 100 different sorts of information recorded. The number of RHS reference sites per 10km square and the period of survey are shown below.

This fact-sheet presents information on a selection of the attributes recorded. The percentage of RHS reference sites with each attribute is presented for the complete network of UK and Isle of Man RHS reference sites, and also for three subsets of sites: England and Wales, Scotland and Northern Ireland. For more meaningful comparison between these subsets, the percentage occurrence of attributes in upland sites is presented separately from that in lowland sites. The small number of upland sites surveyed in Northern Ireland means that these have been omitted from the Northern Ireland column, because meaningful comparison would be difficult - but they have been included in the total (UK and Isle of Man) column. Upland and lowland data for sites in the Isle of Man appear only in the total (UK and Isle of Man) column for similar reasons.

The results in the main Report and this summary fact-sheet need to be viewed with two sources of uncertainty in mind: (i) the observational accuracy of different RHS surveyors, and (ii) the current verification limitations of the RHS database, containing information from the baseline survey. The first uncertainty has been minimised by training and accreditation controls. Secondly, the process of validating the database has involved double-entry and cross checking for errors. Inevitably, some errors will have been missed, but continuing checks will help to ensure that it is fully validated and updated. If results in this summary fact-sheet are to be used for other than broad reporting purposes, the data should be checked with the Environment Agency, SEPA or the Environment and Heritage Service, as appropriate.

	Number of reference sites per 10km grid square	Period of survey	Number of baseline reference sites surveyed		
			Total	Upland	Lowland
England & Wales	3	1994–1996	4559	404	4155
Scotland	1	1995–1996	769	181	588
Northern Ireland	2	1995–1996	266	4	262
Isle of Man	3	1997	18	4	14
Total			5612	593	5019

Attribute	Percentage of RHS reference sites						
	UK & Isle of Man		England & Wales		Scotland		Northern Ireland
	Upland	Lowland	Upland	Lowland	Upland	Lowland	Lowland
Size and predominant valley form							
1 Water width of 5m or narrower	65.0	54.1	67.6	55.2	57.7	50.8	42.6
2 Water width of 5–10m	23.1	22.8	25.0	22.5	19.8	23.9	26.0
3 Water width of 10–20m	8.9	13.2	5.9	12.4	15.9	15.6	21.3
4 Water width greater than 20m	2.5	9.0	1.0	8.9	6.0	9.5	10.1
5 Gorge	3.2	1.7	3.0	1.2	3.8	5.8	0.0
6 Vee-shaped valley	46.6	27.4	46.3	21.4	45.1	49.7	72.9
7 Concave/bowl-shaped valley	22.9	10.8	22.0	10.5	25.8	14.8	6.2
8 Symmetrical (flat) floodplain	7.9	45.8	8.2	51.8	7.7	15.3	19.4
9 Asymmetrical floodplain	13.1	11.1	13.6	11.6	12.6	11.9	1.6
Channel features							
10 1–2 flow types (1995 and 1996 data only)	9.0	43.6	10.8	50.4	4.9	16.1	33.7
11 3–4 flow types (1995 and 1996 data only)	67.2	48.3	68.7	43.6	66.5	65.5	57.8
12 5 or more flow types (1995 and 1996 data only)	22.5	6.4	19.0	3.7	27.5	18.0	8.5
13 Waterfalls or cascades	68.5	21.4	65.3	16.3	74.7	56.0	21.3
14 Rapids	51.3	14.6	48.8	12.0	58.2	38.7	1.6
15 Riffles (1996 data only)	86.2	64.8	85.3	59.0	87.4	84.7	83.1
16 Riffles and pools (1996 data only)	52.6	32.2	52.9	27.2	50.5	51.8	39.8
17 Exposed boulders	87.4	31.6	86.1	23.7	89.6	77.2	51.9
18 Point bars	49.5	32.6	47.3	31.0	54.4	36.2	51.9
19 Mid-channel bars	50.5	29.6	48.8	26.8	54.9	46.0	38.8
20 Coarse woody debris	35.7	51.6	42.3	52.7	22.5	43.8	52.3
21 Extensive coarse woody debris	1.9	3.1	2.0	3.4	1.6	2.7	0.4
22 Debris dam(s) (1995 and 1996 data only)	17.0	18.6	22.0	21.0	9.9	11.0	12.0
23 Fallen trees	31.1	36.8	34.4	36.8	24.7	37.2	35.7
24 Extensive fallen trees	1.5	1.3	1.2	1.3	2.2	1.5	0.0
25 No in-stream channel vegetation, or none visible	26.4	30.8	19.6	30.3	39.6	32.3	31.8
26 1 or 2 types of in-stream channel vegetation	30.5	21.5	28.7	20.4	35.2	30.2	19.4
27 3 or 4 types of in-stream channel vegetation	28.3	26.6	32.7	26.8	19.2	23.6	31.0
28 5 or more types of in-stream channel vegetation	14.8	21.2	19.1	22.5	6.0	13.9	17.8
29 Channel choked with in-stream vegetation	2.4	10.9	2.0	11.8	3.3	7.6	2.7
30 Extensive eroding earth cliffs on one or both banks	8.4	3.5	9.4	3.2	6.6	6.8	1.2
Trees							
31 No trees on either bank	32.5	8.8	29.0	6.7	39.0	21.9	11.6
32 Continuous or semi-continuous trees on: one bank	7.2	19.1	8.2	20.3	5.5	10.5	20.2
33 both banks	26.8	36.5	30.9	36.8	18.1	41.3	20.5
34 Exposed bankside roots	38.0	49.7	42.3	50.4	30.2	46.5	48.8
35 Underwater tree roots	23.4	24.8	30.2	56.5	9.3	25.1	32.9
36 Alders (1996 data only)	24.1	48.3	32.4	51.2	15.3	32.0	64.4
37 Alders suspected of having Phytophthora disease (1995 and 1996 data only)	1.5	1.9	2.6	2.3	0.0	0.5	0.4

Attribute		UK & Isle of Man		England & Wales		Scotland		Northern Ireland
		Upland	Lowland	Upland	Lowland	Upland	Lowland	Lowland
Land use (within 50m of the river channel)								
38 Extensive broadleaf woodland along:	one bank	9.1	15.8	10.4	16.9	6.0	12.1	7.4
39	both banks	7.1	11.9	8.7	10.5	3.8	24.4	5.8
40 Extensive wetland along:	one bank	3.4	2.4	4.5	2.6	1.1	2.0	0.8
41	both banks	4.0	1.5	4.2	1.0	3.8	5.6	0.0
42 Extensive moorland/heath along:	one bank	4.0	0.6	2.2	0.2	7.7	3.1	0.4
43	both banks	27.3	2.1	24.8	0.3	31.9	15.4	0.4
44 Extensive pasture along:	one bank	9.4	23.0	11.9	24.8	4.4	14.8	12.8
45	both banks	18.2	33.4	23.5	34.1	6.6	14.3	67.4
46 Extensive tilled land along:	one bank	9.4	8.1	6.7	7.5	15.4	11.0	11.2
47	both banks	27.9	7.1	22.5	4.5	41.2	25.0	9.3
48 Extensive coniferous plantation along:	one bank	6.2	2.5	5.4	1.6	8.2	8.8	1.9
49	both banks	7.1	1.3	3.7	0.9	13.7	4.1	0.8
50 Extensive suburban or urban land along:	one bank	3.5	10.0	4.5	11.1	1.6	5.3	3.9
51	both banks	1.3	6.2	1.5	7.2	1.1	1.2	0.8
Habitat modification category								
52 "Pristine" channel structure (HMS = 0)		41.8	15.1	38.9	13.6	47.3	28.0	10.1
53 "Semi-natural" channel structure (HMS 0–2)		61.4	29.7	56.9	28.2	70.9	44.3	20.9
54 Channel predominantly unmodified (HMS 3–8)		22.9	21.3	26.0	20.9	16.5	23.8	20.9
55 Channel obviously modified (HMS 9–20)		11.6	20.6	12.1	21.3	10.4	15.1	20.5
56 Channel significantly modified (HMS 21–44)		3.2	24.8	4.0	25.7	1.6	14.9	32.6
57 Channel severely modified (HMS 45+)		0.7	3.5	1.0	3.7	0.0	1.7	5.0
Modifying factors								
58 Straightened channels		0.0	6.2	0.0	7.3	0.0	0.5	0.4
59 One or both banks extensively reinforced		4.9	11.2	6.2	11.3	2.2	7.1	18.6
60 One or both banks extensively resectioned		4.9	31.8	3.7	33.2	7.7	19.4	36.8
61 Weir(s)		8.4	15.0	10.6	15.6	3.3	8.5	19.8
62 Channel extensively embanked on one or both banks		2.7	10.7	2.7	11.0	2.7	7.6	11.2
63 Culvert(s)		3.5	9.3	5.2	10.5	0.0	4.8	3.1
64 Bridge(s)		27.8	43.3	28.2	45.1	27.5	37.0	29.1
65 One or both banks extensively poached		1.7	2.7	2.0	3.0	1.1	1.7	12.8
Invasive alien bankside plants								
66 Giant hogweed		0.3	4.4	0.5	4.2	0.0	4.9	6.6
67 Himalayan balsam		0.3	14.4	0.2	15.8	0.5	4.4	14.0
68 Japanese knotweed		2.4	8.4	3.2	9.2	0.5	3.1	6.6
69 At least one of the invasive alien bankside plants listed in facts 66-68		2.9	23.0	3.7	24.1	1.1	10.4	22.9

Percentage of RHS reference sites

TERMINOLOGY

A full technical glossary can be found in the main Report. Key terms used in this fact-sheet are explained below.

Channel A term used collectively in the Report and this fact-sheet, meaning the course of a river or stream, including the bed and banks. RHS data can, however, be split into channel (in-stream) and bank features.

Extensive The occurrence of a feature or modification along at least one third of an RHS site. This term can be applied to the in-stream channel or to individual banks as required.

HMS (Habitat Modification Score) Modification to the channel, expressed as a score based upon the type and extent of artificial features. The greater the degree of modification and/or level of impact, the higher the score.

Mid-channel bar An exposed river deposit in mid-channel.

Point bar A distinctive exposed river deposit on the inside of a meander bend. Can be unvegetated or vegetated. An important habitat for riverside beetles and other invertebrates.

Rapid An area of broken (white-water) waves associated with steep channels.

Reinforced bank A bank strengthened with concrete, brick or other material to protect it against erosion.

Resectioned bank A bank whose slope has been mechanically reprofiled to enlarge or alter the river channel, thereby increasing flood flow capacity.

Riffle Shallow, fast-flowing water with a distinctly disturbed surface, forming upstream-facing unbroken standing waves, usually over a gravel substrate.

Upland and lowland For the purposes of the main Report and this fact-sheet, **upland** is defined as land over 200m, west of a line between Start Point and Flamborough Head. **Lowland** is defined as land below 200m, including all land east of the Start Point and Flamborough Head line.

Further copies of this fact-sheet are available from the Environment Agency.

For further information, please contact one of the following addresses as appropriate.

Environment Agency
Rio House
Waterside Drive
Aztec West
Almondsbury
Bristol BS32 4UD

Tel: 01454 624400
Fax: 01454 624409
Web site
www.environment-agency.gov.uk

Scottish Environment Protection Agency
Erskine Court
The Castle Business Park
Stirling
FK9 4TR

Tel: 01786 457700
Fax: 01786 446885
Web site
www.sepa.org.uk

Environment and Heritage Service
Commonwealth House
35 Castle Street
Belfast
BT1 1GH

Tel: 01232 251477
Fax: 01232 546600
Web site
www.ehs.nics.gov.uk

ENVIRONMENT AGENCY

SEPA

ENVIRONMENT
AND HERITAGE
SERVICE